Acknowl

Let there be no doubt, this book was inspired and written because of my belief in God, the Father and His son, Jesus Christ. I give praise and thanks for this opportunity to share my writings.

I dedicate this book to my mother, Reather Bryant, for her many prayers and her faith in my abilities. I thank my father, Joseph, for instilling discipline into my every thought. I extend great thanks to my sister, Jenè, and my best friend and brother, Montè, for giving me unforgettable memories and the true desire to succeed. I thank my entire family, especially my grandparents—the late Joseph L. Bryant, Hester Bryant, the late Roscoe Bennett and Claris Bennett—for raising large Christian families and for nourishing my desire to write.

I also thank the talented people that came into my life like angels descending from Heaven: Pia Forbes, Stacy Utley, Ali Nkhazi, Dawn Keene, DW Price, Jon and Alicia Roberts, Mitch Caviness, and George Kelly of Franklin's at Powers Ferry. Your contributions have been nothing short of essential to the completion of this project.

Without the support of many friends, this project would have been impossible. I thank Carol Ingram, Yvette Thompson, Mark Wragg, Lenny Wragg, Craig Campbell, Carol Nichols, D.R. Ingram, Tracy Armstrong, Abdullah Hashim, Ben Bohannon, Kendal Roberts, Kevin Dunston, Cedric Anthony, Roderick Robinson, Greg Worsely, Mike Johnson, Eric McIntosh, Golden Smith, Angela Graham, Kim Boiling, Kellye Whitaker, Danielle Bennett, Surrayah Spears, the late Kiram Anderson, Fairron Newton, Maurice Wilson, and Taylor Thomas.

Finally, I thank all who will take the time to read this book. I pray you understand the many messages this work contains. Thank you, and God bless.

I

Have You Ever Been *Screaming*?

Please take the time to sit down in your most comfortable chair, lay your head back, relax your soul and allow your mind to put your life in review. Make sure you feel your lungs move and your veins tremble. Allow your eyes to close slowly. Remember, quietness is a necessity. Dark rainy evenings create the best results, but on any given day, you can contact your soul; it is always available. When you find tranquility's door, enter with caution.

Many people are afraid to explore soul touching, soul searching, and, as Terry Foster calls it, screaming. Terry defines screaming as the act of hearing souls. The sound of a soul from the past is simply a message for people to hear. Everyone has the ability to hear these sounds, even though the soul's body has long been gone. It is similar to dreaming; when you sleep, you imagine or experience dreams. Well, when you concentrate and meditate effectively, you hear profound thoughts that would probably never surface if you did not meditate. These thoughts are a soul's scream.

Have you ever been screaming?

Family members, in some form or fashion, have influenced everyone. For instance, you may be the only family member in fifty years to have hazel eyes. The soul carries traits similar to how a gene carries a trait. If you take the time and effort to listen to your soul, you will hear lessons experienced by family, friends, or strangers. These lessons are like the instincts of every animal; they are embedded in your soul. Once you get a thought you haven't pondered or you hear a voice other than your conscious voice, then you will be screaming.

Soul touching is a gradual process that takes little energy and an extreme amount of patience. Terry Foster touched his soul and found the gifts of life. Terry learned how to deal with life's challenges as a single man of African descent. The foundations of these lessons can help all men and women. Here is an opportunity to learn about the African-American male through past experiences, poetry,

II

Single
Man
Screaming

A
Novel
By
Jerold Marcellus Bryant

Edited by Pia Forbes
Illustrations by Stacy Utley
Cover Design by Dawn Keene
Typesetting by Dianne's Desktop Typesetting

SMS Marketing & Publishing Company
Smyrna, Georgia

Single Man Screaming workshops, lecturers, speaking engagements and book signings or SMS book on tape or CDs, Inspirational Prose on tapes or CDs, play script or screenplays and shirts, caps and accessories, are available by contacting SMS Marketing and Publishing. These items and books are available at quantity discounts when used to promote products or services. For request/information please write to:

SMS Marketing Division,
P.O. Box 1184
Smyrna, Georgia 30080
Phone # (770) 384-0668 or
Fax to (770) 384-1537

prose and screaming. Here is a view of society's effect on any man's emotions.

Terry, also known as Tee, recognized many situations that were sinful, painful, degrading and stressful. By touching his soul, he found ways to release guilt, gain comfort, and alleviate stress. This screaming process made him a stronger man. The trickle-down effect of screaming influenced friends, employers, lovers, and even enemies. Terry found ways of reshaping his integrity while simultaneously creating an indestructible armor. God is the only one that could destroy Terry's defenses. Accordingly, God is his greatest ally.

Terry's strength and spirituality helped friends through tough times. His soul touching allowed him to discover a writing talent that had gone untapped for twenty years. Terry's strength allowed him to comprehend situations like the perceptions of wise men. Terry is able to understand all aspects of life and death by just screaming.

We all have this gift; Terry just happened to master it. Terry has taken his gift and shared it with others. His purpose is to teach others how to enjoy life and to de-mystify heartbreaking experiences. Screaming is no magical feat, nor is it a power induced by drugs or electrical stimulation. Screaming is powered by faith in God and the ability to identify your soul's purpose.

Women will appreciate the characters' experience while men will say, "I have felt that way before." For those who have not yet experienced similar situations, this will be a guideline on how to cope when you do.

Readers, enjoy. You will be able to relate to Terry's experiences. If problems arise, and you don't know how to solve them, try soul touching, soul searching, or screaming. It works!

Remember! *Enter tranquillity's door with caution, and have God as your ally.*

Jerold M. Bryant

11/22/97

Table of Contents

Table of Contents (continued)

But his delight is in the law of the Lord; and in his law doth he meditate day and night.

And he shall be like a tree planted by the rivers of waters, that bringeth forth his fruit in his season; his leaf also shall not wither and whatsoever he doeth shall prosper.

Psalm 1:2-3

Part One

Terry R. Foster

Chapter 1
The Boy

Terry was still asleep after the "Ooh! Ooh!" of the thirty-one students. This made things worse. Ms. Thomas, the sixth grade teacher had had enough. Terry's head was tucked in the corner of his elbow and forearm and comfortably laid atop of his unopened math book. Terry did not hear Ms. Thomas' threatening remarks. "For those of you who choose to sleep in my class, I have a surprise for you today. Everyone, please let the sleeping beauty lay." Ms. Thomas left the class to go to the office. When she returned, she wore a smile on her face. Thirty minutes later, a woman walked to the door. Ms. Thomas opened the door and pointed towards Terry.

The mother slipped her high heels off and began walking to the back of the class. Some of the students were snickering under the cover of both hands. The mother and Ms. Thomas had no smiles whatsoever. Ms. Thomas held her finger to her mouth and said very softly, "Shhhhhhhhh!"

The mother pointed at Stacey Franklin and motioned for him to get out of his seat. The mother now sat directly behind Terry. The class could not hold their laughs any longer. They burst into a thunderous laugh. Terry still did not move. The mother just shook her head, smiled, and started poking her son in the rib cage with a pencil eraser.

Terry mumbled, "Stacey, stop man." The mother looked at Stacey. Stacey shook his head and laughed.

"That ain't funny man." Terry mumbled again.

The mother took the pencil and slammed it against Terry's head. Terry turned around immediately, frowned like a mad man, and whispered loudly, "Leave me alone!"

Shock, fear and embarrassment registered in Terry's eyes when he realized that Stacey Franklin did not poke his side or hit his head. The classroom erupted with another thunderous laugh. Within seconds, Terry began crying. The mother grabbed his shirt and drug him out of class.

The noise brought the principal out of his office to check on the class. Then the entire school laughed at Terry's expense.

The next week, the mother switched Terry to a more challenging math course, which didn't allow him time to sleep in class. None of his friends were in these classes. Suddenly, it was a different school, not difficult, just time consuming. He only had to read and remember. Terry's grades averaged around a B+.

Terry was very intelligent. He developed a strategy for studying that turned out to be very helpful. Everyday after school, before television and any other form of recreation, Terry read every page of his notes. Pop quizzes were a joke to him. Terry never failed a pop quiz. Terry liked this way of studying. In some cases, he could even write an entire section of his notebook without looking. He realized that if he studied his notes for one hour a day, everyday, he would have studied a solid ten hours for the exams given every two weeks. Then he wouldn't have to cram the week before the exam.

Terry also did his homework as soon as he got it. He figured that if he could finish homework in time to look at his favorite television shows, he would be happy. Sometimes he didn't finish, but most of the time, a great portion was complete.

Six years later, Terry was in the top ten percent of the five hundred member graduating class of Howard High School. This was an admirable finish for a noted troublemaker and former sleeper. It should have been a higher finish, but playing hooky and trying to not look white to black friends really forced Terry to balance two worlds. Sometimes he didn't do his best balancing the peer pressure, but he had a better understanding of the purpose of school.

The summer prior to graduation was a continuous college application completion workshop. He requested applications from every college that interested him. Terry knew he wanted to go to college; he just had to find a college to accept him. Terry quickly learned that he should have started this process in eleventh grade. There was too much pressure to find and decide on the college. He needed more time. The application process and entrance exam fees were expensive, not to mention that the cost of attending a college was even higher. Thanks went to his mother, who had answers for these problems. She requested fee waivers based on financial need and, most times, received them. The SAT and ACT entrance exams were free.

After all campus visits were over and all his questions were answered, Terry narrowed his choices to a predominately white college and a historically black college. Terry's decision was based upon an analogy brought to his attention by his Uncle Jesse.

Two days before Terry's graduation, Uncle Jesse came to town but had not stopped by the house to greet the family. The NBA finals were in the seventh and deciding game. The men of the house were together in the living room watching the television with great anticipation and in silence as the previews of the game started. The men were hoping that Uncle Jesse would find his way to the house before the game started. He always spent his first days in town with his women friends.

"Dre, you think Terry can get on the basketball team when he goes to college?" the old man asked with a smirk, as he laid his head back in his favorite recliner and crossed his legs.

"Dad, it depends on if he ever decides on a college." Dre replied.

"Hey, I just wanna look at the game. I don't wanna hear about college right now," Terry replied.

"Dre, he couldn't walk-on anybody's team with that old ugly jump shot anyway." The old man whispered just loud enough for everyone to hear.

Brring, Brring!

"Saved by the bell. I'll answer the door," Terry said happily.

5

Jerold Marcellus Bryant

Terry walked to the door, peeped through the window, and then shouted with laughter, "Hey! Hey! It's Uncle Jesse with a funky new black Mercedes, y'all !" He quickly opened the door.

"Graduation boy! That's my main man! What's going on, top ten percent?"

"Nothing much, Uncle Jesse, I'm ready to get it over with."

"I'm proud of ya, Terry!"

"Thanks."

Everyone in the house came to the front door to greet Uncle Jesse.

The younger sister jumped into Uncle Jesse's arm and said, "Why did you come here, Uncle Jesse?"

"To see my boy graduate."

"Uncle Jesse, I graduate in six years. You coming to my graduation?" The pretty one asked.

"Yeah! Baby girl! Now get out of my arms. You're too heavy and too old!" Uncle Jesse hollered, "My back, my back, Lord have mercy." Everyone laughed.

As they stood in the foyer, they could hear the game's announcer call the starting line-ups. The game started and all the men ran to the room to get a good seat.

At the dinner table, the father mentioned the favorite topic of the day to Uncle Jesse. "Brother Jesse?"

"Yes, Big brother Joe?"

"If you had a chance to go to a white college or black college, which one would you choose?"

Terry quickly said, "Here we go again."

"Well, you know that I had no choice when I went to prestigious Allen University. I went because of Jim Crow."

"Yeah, that's right" the father replied.

"But I managed to get a good education and a good job. And I own my own business now. So I would have to say, if you take college serious and learn as much as possible, then you will be successful."

The old man said, "Brother Jesse, are you going to answer the question?"

"Naw! I don't want to influence the young man's decision, but I have a perfect analogy for him that should help him decide." Uncle Jesse turned to Terry and said. "Consider that all black people in the United States are subjected to some form of racism. Let's say we are in a boxing match to gain equality. If you decide to go to a white college, you are pretty much still in the fight to gain equality. If you decide to go to a black college, you have a chance to experience what equality is. In other words, you get to sit in the corner away from the actual fight, work on your skills, and be coached before jumping back into the fight. Going to a black college may be the only legitimate chance a black man has to experience liberty in the USA. I think that is the single most important factor between schools that no one can change. The money, courses, and technology can be changed, but no one can change the freedom and equality you experience at our schools."

Terry laughed, then said. "It still ain't an easy decision, Uncle Jesse."

Uncle Jesse laughed and said, "I guarantee the fight against racism will always be there. Equality comes once and a while, and anytime you want to jump back into the fight, it'll be there."

"Damn sure will! Brother Jesse, I like your style." Brother Joe replied with a smile.

After graduation, Terry decided to go to a historically black university based on Uncle Jesse's self-proclaimed perfect example.

College was manageable but a tremendously different story than high school. The first two years were year-long parties that resulted in a "C" average. The next two years were a whirlwind of frantic studying and research to graduate with a business degree. Socializing made it very difficult to graduate with a bachelor's degree in business. "After college, you will get a good job," is what everyone told Terry. He did it, but poor grades with a degree did not add up to a good paying job. Anxiously opened rejection letters for high salary positions laid beside the trash can. The jobs he was offered ranged from bag-boy to cashier to waiter all because he had floundered away his college years. Plans to attend graduate school were created to offset the truth, to cover up the fact that he didn't have a real job.

Even so, a bundle of unopened applications for graduate school lay cast aside on the kitchen counter.

Terry shook his head with disgust. He knew things should have been better. Tee came from a small, country community in South Carolina. He was born, the baby boy of four kids, to Gina and Joe Foster. His older brother named Dre, a sister named Patsy, and a baby sister named Lisa were his immediate family. The rest of the family ran the entire gamut of society. They ranged from successful business owners to politicians to residents of the fifth ward death row in the federal penitentiary. With a hundred relatives in a sixty-mile radius, Terry couldn't have chosen a more tightly knit family than the Foster clan. They were a good old black family out of the backwoods of South Carolina. The nucleus of the family has not moved far from the plantation where Terry's great, great grandfather, Grant, was bought to this land from Ghana.

All Fosters had this understanding that no matter what happened, they would always be proud, supportive, and critical. If someone were wrong, everyone would put his or her two cents worth in the conversation. If someone were right, everyone would be a part of the joy and success. If someone had the audacity to bother a Foster, there would be a war regardless of whom, what, when and where. This family force would come from the jailhouse rift-raft to the police brass.

Overall, Terry's family was well respected by neighbors and the locals of the community. The Fosters would not allow relatives or friends of families to be evicted. They guided young family members in the right direction and insisted that no one leave the nucleus without a good purpose, finance, marriage, college or the bible. Terry remembered when his grandmother threw a house party to raise money for Aunt Cecelia's rent and for Cousin David's first year in college. But house parties occurred less frequently as Grandma got older.

Terry's family loved each other fiercely and considered one another best friends. From Grandmother to Uncle Jesse to cousin Tony to his brother Dre, and his nephew Dre, Jr., Terry loved them all.

Terry had a total of twelve uncles and eighteen aunts. His grandparents needed big families for picking cotton on the farms. Terry's father and his uncle, Jesse, were the so-called leaders of the

Foster clan; they were the oldest and second oldest respectively. Although Uncle Jesse lived in another state, he made every big family gathering.

Tee looked up to Uncle Jesse because he had the great job and made big money. Uncle Jesse was a stockbroker with two undergraduate degrees and a graduate degree. He didn't have a wife or kids, so he was free to go anywhere his money could take him.

Terry knew he was very fortunate to have a father that stayed home, a rare occurrence in his neighborhood. Sometimes Terry and Dre failed to realize that friends looked at them as being abnormal because of the in-house father. They always respected Dad, and Terry gained a lot more respect for his father after he understood the trend of single parent families. But Tee sometimes looked down on his father, especially when they were low on money. Dad didn't graduate from college, he did go for two years until he got bored. Mama always said, "He was a good student, an 'A' student in college."

His parents met in college and married shortly afterward. Two years later they had Dre, and a year and a half later they had Terry. Dad dropped out of school for the family. Mama graduated while Dad worked. Dad worked, made his money, and took care of his family and appeared to be happy. Joe Foster surely was a real man.

Chapter 2
The Man

Terry thought he would never get a chance to prove himself. He thought he would be rejected for the rest of his life. One Monday afternoon after a long day of cleaning office buildings, a job Terry despised, he went to check his mailbox. A stack of letters filled the mailbox. He smiled, picked the mail out of the box and walked back to his apartment. The three letters he opened on the trek to his apartment were denial letters.

Terry stopped at the front door counted the letters and thought, *If all eighteen letters are denial letters, I won't write or send another letter or résumé.* Terry then opened his door entered his apartment laid back in his favorite chair and opened letters. Five minutes later, he was looking at the last three letters. Fifteen letters were denials. He sighed and looked at the cable bill and the student loan letter, thinking, *It's a sad day when bills make you feel wanted.* The last letter was from Wolfe State University; they had turned Terry down after a very good interview three months before. They decided on someone else. Terry was hurt and disgusted because he knew he gave a pretty good showing. Well, Dr. Prickard, the director of admissions wanted Terry to come back and interview for another position.

A smile changed a depressed face but Terry felt humbled because there were no other offers. Pride did not get into his way of interviewing again. He felt he could get the job if he interviewed the way he had the first time. Three weeks later, he entered the office and met the staff again. He interviewed for two hours with almost everyone on the professional staff. This time they had a new face, a black woman named Brenda. She was given the position Terry interviewed for the first time. She was the only black on the professional staff. The interview went as expected smoothly without incident.

It was a week after the interview when Dr. Prickard called Terry to set up a second interview. During the interview, Dr. Prickard talked about salaries. "Terry, the starting salary for all assistant directors is $25,000 per year. This is a non-negotiable salary."

Terry was displeased, "Non-negotiable."

"Yeah, Terry, everyone starts out with this salary." Dr. Prickard replied.

"Well, I'll let you know if I can handle this offer."

Dr. Prickard said, "Well, take a few days, then give me a call. Okay, Terry?"

"Yes, sir, thanks for the opportunity."

Terry left the office depressed because of salary, but was happy to have a legitimate job offer. A few days passed, and Terry looked in his mailbox for new job offers, but denial letters kept coming. He had waited until the last minute. Then left a message on Dr. Prickard's voice-mail, which said, "I have given it plenty of consideration, I will take the job if you haven't offered it to someone else. Give me a call at 394-3823. Thanks."

Terry thought he had waited too long to give Dr. Prickard an answer. When there was no return phone call a week after his message, Terry thought he had lost this job.

It was nearly two weeks after the call when Terry found the letter from Wolfe State in his mailbox. It looked like a denial letter. The letter shook in Terry's hands. He hoped that a good job would bring this long unemployment spell to a welcomed end. Terry prayed, *Please don't be the denial letter that everyone sends.*

He tore into the letter and read the first line. The job was his. Finally the chance to prove his worth to someone. The American dream was fulfilled. It had been a year since a real job. Terry had come from a dead end job with no benefits and no security to landing the dream job. Although the salary was not dreamy, everything else was.

Many of his friends had given up on Terry. Some would say, "He went to school to wait tables." Tee proved them wrong. This job title even made Joe Foster proud of Terry. Terry's father commented, "It's about time."

For the first six months, Terry had to be the docile employee because he was trying his best to learn the position and to learn his new environment. Dr. Prickard and his supporting cast were oblivious to his true viewpoints. Terry just wanted to do his job well, because he had been out of work for so long. He didn't want anything to jeopardize this dream job.

Terry's responsibility was to recruit minority students. He vowed he'd be aggressive in his commitment. Terry knew that his colleagues traditionally dealt better hands to the white students, but he and his co-worker, Brenda, did not know what life lesson lay ahead in their positions. They quickly found out, however, that they were the token blacks in Prickard's positions.

Terry set the stage for his relationship with Brenda Smith when he said, "Right now, we are a team. We have to work together and as far as I'm concerned, you are my sister."

Brenda replied, "Hey, that's great with me. I'm glad I voted on you for the position. I don't need a spineless brother who's afraid to stand up to Dr. Prickard. And I sure don't need a trifling brother trying to make advances on me."

Terry smiled and said, "Hey, you are fine as hell, but we ain't going to do that Anita Hill—Clarence Thomas thing. I got too much to lose."

Brenda replied, "Amen!" She smiled and said, "Excuse me Terry, the 'we ain't' you just used should be 'we are not going to do that Anita Hill-Clarence Thomas thing. Proper English is a necessity in the professional environment."

Terry cut his eyes back at her and said, "Oh so you're that type of sister, huh?" They laughed.

13

Chapter 3
The Awakening

Terry's first appointment on a Monday morning was a walk-in, Mr. Darryl Johnson. Office protocol assigned walk-ins to the officer-of-the-day who handled impromptu customer service situations. Christine Collins, the officer-of-the-day, was not interrupted because Darryl Johnson was a black student, and she was white. The administrative assistants made it their business to keep the black students with the black advisors. This would not have been a problem if all the white students had been directed to the white advisors, but that was never the case.

Darryl was the first of many interruptions that morning. The assistant buzzed the phone, "Mr. Foster, there is a walk-in with special interest who's filling out an information sheet."

"I'll be ready in five minutes."

The assistant brought the information sheet and apologized for bypassing the officer-of-the-day. Terry mentioned, "We need special interest training for all officers of the day."

She laughed. Terry refused to crack a smile.

A quick preview of Mr. Johnson's information showed he grew up in the projects. He graduated from Smith High School, a predominately black school known for its athletes, not its academics. He was interested in majoring in engineering. Darryl was not an athlete, and he did not take any college prep, honors or advance placement courses. He had not taken the SAT, which should be taken several times before a student enters the twelfth grade. Before he even entered the office Terry thought, *I'm probably going to have to steer him into another college or community college. He won't have the scores to get into this university.*

The administrative assistant pointed in Mr. Johnson's direction as Terry entered the lobby area. Mr. Johnson stood with application in hand and the daunting intimidating look that many young black males displayed. Terry called this look "the gangster grit." Mr. Johnson wore jeans two sizes too large and hanging off his rear-end, a designer athletic sweater two sizes too large, and a cap atop of his head. If Terry had not been accustomed to being with young black people, or in other words, if Tee were white, he probably would have been worried about this appointment. Mr. Johnson looked too "ethnic" for Tee's conservative colleagues. He was of medium build, around six feet tall and weighed around two hundred pounds. Terry quickly sized him up because if Mr. Johnson lived up to his mean gangster grit, Terry would have to take him to the grass and show him his fighting skills. Terry could tell that the kid was a scrapper, by the scars on the face and hard-core expression he wore. The young man easily could have passed for twenty-five when, in fact, he had just turned seventeen.

"Mr. Johnson, how are you doing?" Terry extended his hand.

"All-right, I mean fine, sir." He shook Terry's hand.

Terry noticed that Mr. Johnson lacked the polished professional handshake. So he gave a discrete immediate lesson for the young brother. Terry gripped his hand tighter and firmer. Mr. Johnson tightened his grip. Terry smiled. Terry thought, *Welcome to the real world, Mr. Johnson.*

"I'm Terry Foster, Assistant Director of Admissions. Why don't you follow me back into my office?" Terry could tell by the relief in the gangster grit that Mr. Johnson wanted a black person as his advisor.

They entered Terry's office, Terry asked him to take a seat. Mr. Johnson sat down.

"Before we get started, Mr. Johnson, you need to take that cap off your head while you're in my office."

"Oh, Mr. Foster, I'm sorry, I forgot!"

Terry grinned, "No problem."

"Now, what can I do for you today, Mr. Johnson?"

"I want to come here for college." Darryl's eyes never came in contact with Terry's eyes. Darryl handed Terry an application with transcripts and scores. They noticed the envelope shook with nervousness when Darryl handed over the material. Terry thought, I *intimidated him.* Terry quickly stopped the professional approach. Terry closed the door and pressed the Do Not Disturb button on the phone. He looked at Mr. Darryl Johnson and spoke in a comforting, brotherly voice.

"Hey man, check this out. You have no reason, no reason at all, to be nervous around me. I am here to help you. The second thing you need to do is look me in the eyes when we talk O.K.?"

Darryl raised his head, looked Terry in the eyes and said, "Yes, sir!"

Darryl took a deep breath, exhaled, smiled and looked assertive. Terry knew he had made a true connection, when he dropped the professional approach and got real with this young man.

Terry opened the envelope. Surprisingly, the application was typed. *Probably by the mom,* Terry thought. The transcripts did not show his SAT scores. A note from the guidance counselor stated that Darryl was scheduled to graduate this year. Terry quickly looked for the grade point average. Darryl had taken his four years of English, math, science and social sciences and made "C's" and "D's" throughout. Terry had assumed correctly. Darryl had a 2.0 grade point average, which probably would be even lower after he took a few technical courses that didn't figure into the evaluator's grade configurations.

Terry looked at Darryl and asked him, "Did you find high school hard or easy?"

Darryl took a moment and said, "Easy. I never put in the time I needed. I could have done a lot better."

Terry quickly asked, "Then why didn't you?"

Darryl shrugged his shoulders, "I don't know."

Shrugging his shoulders as Darryl had, Terry quickly replied, "That same 'I don't know', shows up in your transcripts. It says to me,

'I don't know' how to make good grades." Terry shrugged his shoulders.

"It says, 'I don't know' how to manage my time." Terry shrugged his shoulders. "It says to me, 'I don't know' much about these classes I have taken over the last four years." Terry shrugged his shoulders and opened his hands.

"It tells me you don't know a lot of things." Terry shrugged his shoulders for the last time with hands open, pointing towards the ceilings.

Tee felt himself on the podium, so he eased off a little. "The only thing that you have proven to me is that you care about getting out of high school just by the hair of your chinny-chin-chin. And now you want to get into this college, and you think that talking to the right people will help you get what you want. Am I right?"

Darryl shook his head in the up and down manner, "Yes, sir."

Terry looked at him and asked, "Did your Mama send you here today?"

Dejected, he shook his head side to side.

"Answer me."

"No, sir."

This impressed Terry beyond belief.

"Well, who or what made you come here today?"

"Mr. Foster, I wanted to come here." He paused.

Terry questioned him again, "You decided?"

Darryl shaking his head, said with a smile, "I did!" He had come to a realization.

Terry's outlook on Darryl changed when Darryl took ownership of his actions. No one had gotten him out of bed. He decided that he wanted an answer. He would not allow anyone to get in his way. He was not going to leave before someone counseled him about his future. He finally faced reality. Something finally clicked that it was time for him to be a man. It was time to take care of business. Darryl had heard enough of his mother and her bickering about his attitude and actions.

That very morning, Darryl took control, and Terry was proud of him.

Terry's presentations to prospective students who visited campus focused on a favorite quote from a colleague, "Failure to realize reality invites your own destruction." Terry made students understand what this statement meant. Terry asked Darryl "Explain it." Darryl said, "Get ready, or you're finished."

Terry quickly asked, "Are you getting ready today?"

"I've been trying to find out what I need to do to get into college. I wanna be successful and get a good job."

Terry knew that Darryl did not have the grades to get into many schools. Heck, Darryl probably wouldn't survive one week on campus. So Terry had to find a way to deny this kid and keep his spirits up. Terry did not want to be the reason for him to give up. Especially when Darryl had just realized one important aspect of being a man: **initiative**.

Terry took time to review Darryl's record. He looked at his numbers and acted as though he calculated a new grade point average. Terry left the office and got information about community colleges, great avenues for students who struggled. Terry also pulled together things related to Darryl's first choice of majors and information on financial aid.

Afterwards, Terry looked at him and said, "I'm going to give you this application fee back, because if I take it, you will be out of fifty-five dollars. I don't want to waste your money. Right now you have no chance of getting into this school without attending a community college, first."

Darryl said dejectedly, "Thanks." Then he began to rise from his chair.

Tee stopped him immediately. "Hold on! I haven't finished! You don't need to leave out of here without knowing what you need to do. I'm going to take extra time with you and point you in the right direction. So that you can have a chance to go to almost any college you can afford to go to. Plus, I saved you fifty-five dollars, so you have to listen. You owe me."

Terry gave Darryl everything, as though he were his little brother. Terry explained what needed to be done step by step. The general stuff every student needs to know such as getting the application or the financial aid forms in the offices on time. No procrastination. Terry showed him the quick and dirty way to prepare for the SATs and how to study to get a "B" or better in community college classes.

Terry told him if he ever has any questions, "I am available." Terry even mentioned, "I have great contacts at these colleges and universities. If you keep that same will and attitude that got you in my office this morning, call me and I will help."

Darryl paused, looked over the paperwork, and shook his head in the affirmative.

"After four years, you'll have a degree hanging off your wall. Now you know what you need to do. I can help you only so much."

His simple response was, "Man, that's all right. Thanks, Mr. Foster."

Exactly one hour after his impromptu visit, Terry walked Darryl out of his office into the hallway. Darryl, with cap in hand and book-bag on his shoulders, extended his hand.

Terry shook his hands and noticed that Mr. Johnson had a firm grip. Terry smiled, pulled him closer and gave a half hug with a pat on the back as they shook hands. Terry whispered in his ear, "Don't lose focus."

Darryl shook his head up and down as though he understood.

The secretaries and administrative assistants witnessed this exchange.

Ann, one of the administrative assistants, commented, "Mr. Foster, aren't you glad I gave you that appointment?"

Terry replied, "Yeah, good decision."

One thought stayed with Terry. He realized that he was one of the last chances Darryl had to get on the right path. Before Terry accepted his dream position, he had been angered by all the negative media attention black male youth received. However, his eagerness to fit in and be accepted by his colleagues had blinded him to his goals. When Darryl walked into his office he saw the same person his white colleagues would have seen—an at-risk kid. He quickly relayed his erroneous thoughts and faced his own fault— the fact that he had assumed the I'm-greater-than-thou complex.

Terry recognized that the I'm-greater-than-thou complex was a dilemma that no successful man of color in the United States should possess as long as rebel flags flew and institutional racism existed. Terry realized that there was a reason for the many stories on our news stations and newspapers. There was a real reason why these problems existed in our society, and there was a real solution. The solution lay in regulation or eliminating the I-am-greater-than-thou complex.

Darryl reminded Terry of himself and friends whose demeanor and habits were very similar. At one time, Terry procrastinated, assuming that when he was ready to be an adult, things would fall into place. Then his parents straightened him out. Some of Terry's friends had served six years in the Dallas Penitentiary System. One said to Terry, "When I get out, I'll be ready." Terry always thought, *Yeah, right.*

Terry couldn't relate to everything Darryl had gone through, but he did understand that Darryl needed a father figure to help him become a real man. Terry thought to himself, *I would be the best big brother for Darryl. Not the father type, like Dad, but a good big brother.*

Chapter 4
Veronica

Her soft knock on the opened door did not get Terry's attention, but the voice from Heaven did.

"Excuse me?"

Terry quickly brought his head from the paper work, startled by the unfamiliar voice.

"I'm sorry, sir, I'm looking for the graduate school admissions office."

Terry's eyes beheld the most beautiful woman that he had ever seen. Terry replied. "I wish I could help you, but they are upstairs in room seventeen." Veronica had entered his office by mistake.

"Thank you."

Terry got up from his desk. "Hey, Miss!"

"Yes," she replied, turning back towards the office.

"What are you going to major in?" He leaned on the front of the desk.

"I'm trying to get my MBA."

"Oh, that's great. Are you from Raleigh?"

"No, I'm from DC."

"So you're visiting here, just to check out some schools?"

"Yeah, I'm here for two days."

Terry smiled. "Since you're visiting, let me ask you out for dinner."

She paused, "Well, go ahead, Mr. Foster, ask."

Terry noticed her observance. "So she can read name tags."

"Yeah, I sure can."

"Would you like to go out for dinner, um, Ms...? What's your name?"

"Veronica Sellers."

"Would you like to go out for dinner, Veronica? Let's say tonight around seven o'clock." Terry gave her his patent smile.

"No, Thank you. Mr. Foster, Good bye." She said sharply.

"Oh! That's cruel!" Terry laughed.

She laughed and walked away, leaving Terry in a quandary. Terry thought, *She's good.*

Terry took a step into the hallway to look at Ms. Sellers' entire package. She was perfect. About five feet, nine inches tall. Beautiful brown skin with a summer tan and a figure sculptured by God's top designer.

As she walked down the hallway, Terry shook his head in amazement. She turned around, saw her admirer, and laughed again. Dr. Prickard and his associate director Paul Rue were walking to the office as they passed the beauty queen. Both of them greeted her and watched her waltz to the stairs. Veronica Sellers was the best-looking woman to ever grace the office while Terry was there. Terry made it his position to never approach a female at work. But she was the exception to the rule. He did not feel guilty for his actions.

The rejection fueled Terry's fire for thirty to forty minutes, then he calmed down. Every person that passed his door received attention from him for the next two days. She did not come back. Terry thought, *Damn! She's a mean old hag.*

A week passed and Terry thought about Veronica more than a few times. *I'll meet her again.*

Part Two

Testing the Waters

Chapter 5
First Steps to Manhood

Uncle Jesse whispered in little Terry's ears as they embraced, "Terry, whatcha doing for yourself, boy?" Terry didn't know how to answer. He was only four years old; Tee generally did what his parents wanted. Tee whispered back in his ear, "Trying to get paid, Uncle Jesse!" This was a reply that the Dad always used when he greeted his friends.

Uncle Jesse belted out a big laugh and hugged Tee, scratching his face with his rough, gray stubble. "Just like your old man, just like him." Then he dug into a fancy leather billfold packed with greenery and handed Terry five dollars. Tee immediately said "Thanks." He then ran and teased his brother, Dre, about his treasure.

They never saw Uncle Jesse as much as they wanted, but when he came to town, it was always a celebration. Uncle Jesse was the type of man that kept people laughing, drinking, and talking. He never seemed to stay long enough. His dad, Joe Foster, and Uncle Jesse would always find time to spend together; sometimes they would go out and come back in the early mornings, tripping and falling, laughing and snickering all over the house. This behavior was never the norm for his dad, but it became regular for about two weeks after Uncle Jesse's visit. The memory of those two weeks lingered in Tee's mind from the age of four.

Sitting by the kitchen window, staring into the raindrops for answers, Tee blurted out questions about

27

everything from pregnancy to death. Tee was bored with nowhere to play and nowhere to go but anxious to make things happen. And boy did they happen!

"Mama, where's my daddy?" Tee asked.

She mumbled somberly, not intending for Tee to hear, "Baby, your daddy died a long time ago."

Scared and troubled by this answer, Terry ran to his parents' room to find his father stone asleep, but not dead. Tee had never known his mom to lie, but she was telling a big one that day!

As Tee returned to the kitchen, puzzled, he said, "Daddy is alive, he ain't dead, he been alive all my life!"

She laughed after he stated his case. "Tee, that's not bad for a four year old. I meant to say he's dead asleep," she said.

"I'm almost five," Tee replied without hesitation.

Her laughter ceased. She sat Terry on the counter and said, "Tee, as long as you live, I want you to treat every girl better than your daddy treats me."

Apparently they had been in yet another argument. Tee figured his dad was still a player, or a rolling stone, or wanted to be like Uncle Jesse. At least, that's what his mother always said.

"Gina! Gina!" Dad's base voice shook the rafters and his big feet plowed the floors. "Why is Tee running around this house like a bat out of hell? Y'all know I gotta get some sleep before work. Tee! Boy! What I tell you 'bout sittin' on that counter?"

Terry jumped to the floor and ran to see what Dre was doing. Terry took his Mama's commandment to heart. Terry became a different man. Terry would be better than his dad when it came to his wife! He would be better than his friends' dads who were generally missing in action. Tee surely didn't want anyone thinking that he died while he was still living.

Many years later, Tee finally understood what his mama meant. One day after a stressful day of work, he wanted to unwind. So Tee decided to sit in his most comfortable chair. He turned the television, the radio, and the lights off. Terry loosened his tie and took his shoes off. Terry always enjoyed this time by himself, but this day would be different.

He laid his head back, closed his eyes, and searched and listened for complete quietness. Terry could hear only his breathing. No other noise existed. There seemed to be too many topics surfing through his thoughts. Terry was thinking about everything from girlfriends to new clothing to spending money for car insurance. But he wanted to explore a new realm of thinking. He wanted serene thoughts with new meaning. So Terry asked God to take him back to his first comprehensible memory of life. He took Terry back to that time twenty-five-years ago when his parents were recovering from Uncle Jesse's visit. This time, Tee had an adult's perspective. He was able to grasp the entire atmosphere in that house and understand his mama's response. He felt everything she felt. He heard more than her response to his question, "Mama, where's my daddy?" Terry felt her thoughts, her reasoning, and her frustrations, which formed her response, "Baby, your daddy died a long time ago." Her answer, although callous, was a fitting answer for African-American women trying to figure out African-American men.

Terry hadn't known the details of why they were upset that morning. He assumed it was because his dad hadn't come in the previous night. His parents normally kept the door to their room closed. So his question was not a childish, far-fetched attempt to gain information or attention. Her answer included what the consensus of African-American women felt—morbidly helpless.

Terry believed this was the first time he heard a soul while being conscious. Sometimes he would hear souls in a good hard sleep, but he attributed them to dreams. After an hour of this unusual type of meditation, Terry got his journal and wrote about his soul touching experience. Terry was amazed that he could hear or feel his mother's thoughts twenty-five years later, but these voices or messages transcended through time. Her soul sort of screamed. His mama's stern statement about treating every woman better than his dad treated her was probably the most important social lesson he learned at that age. It became a way of life! When he mentioned the occasion to her, she vaguely remembered. Then he let her read the passage from his journal.

"Read this, Mama. Tell me what you think."

After reading the passage, she stuttered, "Ah! Ah! Terry Foster! You're a mind reader!"

Astonished by what she said, Tee shrugged it off saying, "Yeah, right! I wish."

"No! Tee, I'm serious baby!" An intense look on her face, she grabbed his hand.

She then said, "I used to feel like this about your daddy and all the sorry-behind black men in the world, especially Uncle Jesse." Mama shook her head, smirked and continued, "It always seemed like your daddy could have been a better man if he had taken his time to know the Lord."

"I hated when he stayed out in the streets. I'll never forget the time before Jesse was headed to New York. He left this house to go get his cigarettes and stayed out until about five o'clock the next morning. Your daddy woke up mad that morning because the kids were running all over the house."

She shook her head again and said, "Yeah, I remember that feeling like it was yesterday."

Then, in her charismatic way, to change the subject she said, "Tee, I didn't know you kept a journal or that you wrote poetry."

Terry's reply was, "Neither did I. This is my first journal entry and my first poem."

Mama said, "Well, keep it up Tee, you might like writing. This entry has touched me deeply."

"Yeah, I probably will stick with it for a while."

Tee thought about how simple it was to record his Mama's thoughts of his childhood memory. This meditation and writing process became a habit of sorts, and before he knew it, he was recalling hundreds of things in his past, present and future. Terry termed this meditation process screaming, hearing souls from the past. The poems, passages and short stories were records of his screaming.

Inspiration #1

December 25, 1971

Mama, where's my daddy?
Baby, your daddy died a long time ago

I met your daddy in hard times
He represented every Black man
He struggled just as before
But now he is weaker than other men truly know
Baby your daddy died a long time ago

He died on slave ships; he died on the rope
He died by white hands, he died by dope
He died in the fields; he died with dreams
Baby your daddy died a long time ago.

Death took four hundred years; removed from the motherland
Where he used to be a strong, strong African
His culture, his home, his language, his tone
Changed for the worst, before he had known
Walking like a zombie with no heart and no blood
Killing his own brother with ride-bys and the white man's slugs

By the crack of a whip, by the pull of a trigger
Always known as the white man's nigger
He came strong with fight in his arm
But he never heard God's alarm
God said, "Don't worry about problems, I am the solution"
Your daddy lost the faith in all the confusion

Baby your daddy died a long time ago,
Your daddy died a long time ago!

Chapter 6
The Fatherly Promise

All of Terry's friends liked Uncle Jesse. Many idolized him. They'd always ask, "When is your uncle coming to town?"

Uncle Jesse was one of few men who would try to play with them. Sometimes he'd buy them candy and tease them just enough to let them know they were significant to him. Unlike the other men in the area, he took time to see what was happening in their lives.

Mama and her best friends, Ms. Shirley and Ms. Dee, always used to talk about Uncle Jesse. Those ladies, over gossip, would help shell many brown paper bags full of beans. Sometimes Tee would sit down and help with shelling beans and listen to them talk. Tee got into a lot of conversations, making piecemeal additions. Then one day, Tee mentioned that all his friends wanted to be like Uncle Jesse.

Ms. Dee replied, "The fruits don't fall far from the tree!"

Ms. Shirley fell over her pot of shelled beans, laughing hysterically.

Terry's mother quickly said, "Dee!" and gave her the stern look she regularly reserved for Dre or Tee.

Ms. Dee recanted as Ms. Shirley kept on laughing. She said, "Tee, your Uncle Jesse is a good man!"

It took me some time to figure out that Ms. Dee's reply was about the illegitimate kids Uncle Jesse supposedly had.

Tee never thought that Uncle Jesse could be mean enough to leave or never claim his children. Uncle Jesse seemed like he would be the coolest father any one could have. He was definitely mild-tempered compared to Tee's father. Tee personally liked to assume that Uncle Jesse didn't know about his kids. Tee assumed that if Uncle Jesse had known, then he would have been a proud father.

When Terry's best friend, Vince, said his girlfriend was pregnant, Terry thought of young Uncle Jesse. The Uncle Jesse Tee imagined would have acted like Vince, the soon-to-be father. Vince and Lisa had been dating for almost four years, and the couple found themselves forced to make a decision. They decided to keep the baby and married sometime after his birth. Ironically, Terry's girlfriend, Queva, told him the same news: she was pregnant. Although Vince and Terry took different routes, Tee always thought about this period of his life. Terry found Vince's soul during this time, and it was his favorite screaming expedition. One day after work, Terry heard Vince's soul scream for hours, going on about the joy of fatherhood. Afterwards, Tee literally felt like a father.

Men can react several different ways when a woman says, "Baby, I think I'm pregnant," "I'm having your baby," or "It's your baby." After the shock wears off, he might think about commitment, financial security, plans and love. Or he could think about freedom, fear, escape and set-ups. These are the most incredible feelings a man can experience. Sometimes he is simply so confused that he thinks, *Life has changed forever.*

A loving father will stay in contact with his child before and after it is born. After all the numbness wears off, a sense of pride takes over. The loving father will lose perspective, sometimes over-emphasizing the care of the fetus instead of showing tender loving care to the woman. Pregnancy is his new project, and he is excited. His service rating will decrease as she nears the seventh month because he is getting tired. The novelty is wearing off, but he trudges on patiently.

A loving father will tell his friends/family/strangers that she is expecting. That is, *if it is a relationship that is structured for disclosure.* He will be with her as much as possible, as long as needed. The pride of his existence lies in his unborn child. The question that looms in his mind is, *'Will God bless me with the responsibility?'*

God's gift comes after long months of pondering. The new daddy looks at the newborn with comparative eyes. He knows that the child, a miraculous mirror of two people, is innocent and has a natural need for help. The loving father makes his fatherly promise to the child through God, the interpreter, and is bonded to this child forever. The loving father says, "That's my baby" to the world.

Vince called Terry the same day he received a copy of a passage Terry wrote in his journal. He said, "Tee, when I first saw Little Vince, I was the happiest man alive. When we got home, I made a promise to always be near because he's my baby. I counted the toes. I even challenged the boy to a game of one on one before he opened his eyes. Your poem hits it right on the head, Tee! You been gettin' high or something?" Vince asked jokingly.

Terry replied, "Man, you know I don't mess with that stuff!" Upbeat, Terry explained, "I was just thinking about Little Vince and realized that I would have had a kid close to his age. Hey, I might even be married." Vince laughed.

Then Terry said, "Queva and I could've had ...,"

Vince finished his sentence emphatically saying, "Nothing but headaches!"

Vince sucked his teeth. Terry imagined Vince rolling his eyes, staring at the phone as if to say, *We will not be talking about Queva. I have heard enough about that chick.*

"It wasn't supposed to be, so don't get ruffled about it," said Vince with a note of sincerity.

Terry laughed, and Vince changed the subject.

Screaming the times Terry had with Queva proved to be very difficult and draining for him.

Hindsight proved that Vince's choice was the best decision. Terry, on the other hand, made a poor decision—abortion. Terry eliminated all chances of life. Uncle Jesse's decision not to father his kids was a poor decision and could have been corrected through financial responsibilities or good, old-fashioned quality time. According to Ms. Dee's remarks, Terry would have been missing some friends if Uncle Jesse had had the right to abort. Terry, too, should have stood up and accepted the challenges of manhood. Terry believed that abortion was the single most selfish act known to man. He learned through the meditation /screaming process that Queva and he were concerned about themselves only. They had what Terry called the "I complex." Every reason to terminate was based on Terry and or Queva: "I can't do this…" "I don't have that…" "I would not be able to do…" "I'd be forced to do…" and "I'd be treated differently if I had a baby." They should have taken "I" out of their reasons and focused on the greatest gift of all: life.

Screaming Vince's soul helped Terry to see what mistakes he made, what rewards he missed, and, most importantly, how selfish he was.

Vince was Terry's age but more mature than Terry. Terry was disappointed that maturity did not come his way, especially because it seemed to come so easy for Vince. Terry never accepted responsibilities or commitment as a man should. In the case of children and a wife, he definitely failed. He was not ready. He was thinking that some better option would come along.

Did the Angels Cry?

Did the angels cry when you left Heaven?
Tons of tears rained on the earth
As you entered my hands
God's greatest gift in a sinful land

You bring a winter warmth in this chest of mine
You make the lonely pains disappear with a smile
When survival of the fittest tends to be God's will
I take great pride in your existence to make my life fulfilled

The angels must have cried a billion tears
Because I could smile a billion years
I gained a prize that no one can compare
I will love you beyond your time, with no despair

My child, do your best to get to Heaven
And live God's words in days of seven
I will help you gain this discipline
However, you make the choice
To live in the skies again

And I shall shed tears of joy
As the angels rejoice in thunderous noise
As the passage of life takes its toll
The Lamb will bless your unblemished soul
Giving reason to why the angels cried that day
Giving reason to why my smile never went away

Inspiration #3   January 18, 1988

That's My Baby

I'm amazed by your little feet, little hands, no teeth
Bald head, some with hair
A natural beauty, we've all been there

Eyes open, some are closed
But no need to worry, you got ten toes
Crying for days must be from your Mama's side
Tear up stuff, and I'll tan your hide

I can't wait until you're old enough to play
I'm going to win all the time
I might let you win one day!

You laugh and smile or stare into space
You know when to eat, but for now I'll say the grace

Noises you make are sometimes too loud
But even the smallest sound can bring a crowd
The smell of powder after a good stench
Brings relief to noses who call it innocent
Everyone wants to touch you, to make you react
Even when you sleep, we tend to double check
The day must be long when you have all the attention
You're always on someone's mind, or people like to mention
So and so has a baby, did you know?
I'm not surprised; everyone feels your glow!

Now, Daddy has to go to make the money, flow
And, because you're my baby
My family will continue to grow
Now go to sleep and have no fear
I won't go far, I'll be here
Now go to sleep and have no fear
I won't go far, I'll be near
I'll be back and that's no maybe!
Everyone knows you're my BABY!

Inspiration 4#   January 16, 1988

Please Don't

Please don't
ABC your way out of this situation, it's too easy

Or find the popular reasons to justify
Money, timing, marriage and not in love is no tie
When life is on the line
You were a child and you were a gift

Please don't
ABC your way out of this situation, it is too easy
Or the reality sets in
That the reality sat in you

Please don't
ABC your way out of this situation; it is too easy
Please don't, it's too easy

Chapter 7
Screaming to the Music

After many screaming expeditions, Terry started testing his skills with minor distractions, such as television, radio, and lights. The shoes always stayed off. The pen in his hand and the journal locked under his forearm became required tools. Terry wanted to record these thoughts while he was fresh from the expedition.

One of the most incredible things happened when Terry was screaming with music for the first time. He found connections with two musicians that epitomized manhood and strong will. The first musician came to him accidentally. Terry felt his vibe by listening to the radio. At the exact moment when Terry finally relaxed his body and soul and started soul searching, a horn played in the song. Terry didn't remember the name of the song, or the rhythm, or the exact type of instrument, but Louis Armstrong's scream collided with Terry's screaming expedition.

Perhaps someone in his family spent plenty of special time with Louis Armstrong. Maybe a family member revered Louis and passed the memories to him as part of the DNA package. Somehow, Terry had imagined himself as a good friend of Louis Armstrong. He felt as though they had a genetic connection of sorts, and the image or memory of talking to this man startled Terry. After all, Terry had never heard a Louis Armstrong song in his entire life.

It was an unusual occurrence. Terry was dressed in white slacks, an explosive orange tight-fitting shirt, an old style straw hat, a brown belt and expensive brown leather sandals. The patio view extended over four hundred feet of plush green grass. Adjacent to the patio was a figure-eight pool full of sky blue water reflecting the sun's rays. At the end of the plush grass, the blue ocean crashed into an endless strip of white sand and boulders. Terry was enjoying the view. He held in one hand a daiquiri and a smooth, warm hand the other. She wore a white sundress, a straw hat on her head and an explosive orange belt around her waist. Terry hesitated to say that she looked like Dorothy Dandrige or Tina Turner. Not because it would be an exaggeration, but because he didn't want someone to think of being related to Ike. They sat, protected by the shade of an umbrella, at the glass patio table, looking into each other's eyes. Terry thought he was dreaming until Louis came and sat right beside them and started blowing smooth sounds from his trumpet. Terry could feel his hands clapping as Louis finished his last notes. When Louis finished, he set the trumpet on the table. Terry said something like *Great job!* and shook his hand. As his hand rose to grasp his, Terry caught a glimpse of a face in the reflection of his trumpet. Terry looked harder, trying to decipher the skewed reflection, but before he could see the face clearly, someone knocked at his door, and he snapped back into reality.

The interruption felt like a dreaded commercial break in the middle of the movie. The salesman trying to sell magazine subscriptions received the brunt of Terry's frustration. Tee snapped, "I don't want anything! I have Sports Illustrated, Ebony, and Jet. Don't come back!"

Terry tried to get back to Louis, but he had lost his composure, and he really didn't know what triggered the thought. Terry quickly wrote this experience in his journal. He felt proud to have had a chance to scream with Louis. Terry later wrote his experience.

Inspiration #5   February 5, 1990

I Feel Proud

I feel proud to be with Louis
Hear his trumpet blow!

Sounds of black people's souls
It's good for the new and the old

Hear his manly laugh, what a comforting sound it was
Lets you know you're listening to jazz from up above

I feel proud to be with Louis
To hear that trumpet sound
To hear the raspy voice
To see the sun go down

Hear that trumpet blow; hear the Armstrong sound
He's playing Heavenly music on Heaven's ground

I feel proud to be with Louis
Just imagine his smile
The man, the music, the persona
What a blessed style
I feel proud to be with Louis
Hear that trumpet sound!

Frustrated with his commercial break, Terry quickly tried to redirect his musical experience by playing Bob Marley's *Redemption Song,* which happened to be his favorite. He put the CD player on repeat and threw himself into screaming process with intensity.

After about forty minutes, he heard Marley's soul scream. It was mind-blowing! It was powerful! It was unmistakably the most directed informational screams Terry had ever heard. The strength of Marley's words catapulted Terry into a new realm of screaming that encompassed learning for all peoples. Marley's music was the inspiration for Terry's journey into the true horrors of the world, the history of black people, the impetus for redeeming their pains and using of God in his search to help solve the problems of the black man and society. The most important theme Terry heard in this Marley scream was that he had to know himself before he could help anyone else.

Terry was eager to see what was written in his journal. To his surprise, he had no entry in the form of poetry, prose, songs, nothing! *Redemption Song* was already a scream from Bob Marley's soul. There was nothing else to write.

Chapter 8
Church Shakings

Terry went to work early on Friday morning so he could get eight hours in and leave work at four o'clock instead of five o'clock. When he got to work, the support staff had already opened the office. The secretaries were anxious to start the weekend also. Terry greeted them as usual. He went to check his mailbox. There was a card inside. Terry opened it with curiosity. It read:

> Mr. Foster,
>
> I would like to invite you to church on Sunday. Eleven o'clock at West Ministries Church. I'd rather get to know you this way.
>
> Please meet me at your office parking lot area at ten thirty Sunday morning. I will be driving a white Saab.
>
> Don't be late. I look forward to seeing you.
>
> Sincerely,
> Veronica

Terry took a deep breath, smiled, and said, "What a way to start the day!" The secretaries picked their heads up to see what he was talking about. Terry smiled and said, "It's Friday ! Be happy."

Terry was up at nine o'clock anxiously awaiting his chance to meet Veronica. He selected his best navy blue suit and his black leather shoes, crisp, pearl white French-cuffed shirt, gold cuff links and the best silk tie he owned—a vivid red. He was shaven and smelling good from head to toe. Halfway to the car, he made a U-turn and went back to get his bible. He did a double-check in his rear view mirror, cranked his car, and was on his way. Terry was so anxious to have a chance to meet her again that he was five minutes early.

As he drove into the parking lot, he saw the white Saab. It was not a cruel joke. She smiled when he got out of the car and said, "Good to see you."

"Good to see you too, Ms. Sellers."

"I'll drive. Do you have everything?" Veronica asked.

"Yeah, I've got everything."

Just as they got out of the parking lot, Terry told Veronica, "Stop, I forgot my bible." She laughed and said, "Mr. Yeah-I-Got-Everything."

Then she said, "The purpose of this meeting is to worship the Lord, not date. Okay?"

Terry replied, "Amen!"

They drove with the roof down to church. The radio's gospel music made the only sound.

She looked beautiful in her summer red dress. Her long black wavy hair pulled into a ponytail made her look as though she were fifteen years old. Terry thought, *She looks great. Thank you, Lord!*

The choir was on the outside of the church waiting for the last of the congregation to enter. As they pulled into the church parking lot, Veronica said, "I'm singing in the choir today, so you'll have to sit by yourself this time. It'll help you get focused."

"You could have told me that, Ms. Sellers. From now on you need to inform me of matters like this."

"You're right I should have told you, but I'll tell you why I didn't later. Enjoy."

She entered into the line outside of the church with the massive choir dressed in white robes and red tassels. She put on her robe and smiled as Terry looked at her from the front door. He

46

entered the church lobby wearing a serious face. The choir members' shoes scraped the concrete as they lined up behind Terry and the few people in the lobby. The ladies were anxious to enter the church, and everyone was humming a song and clapping as he entered the church. The usher opened the sanctuary doors and started handing out the programs.

The church was packed. The church was quaint and beautifully decorated. The two story building had a balcony, red carpet, and mahogany pews. The lighting made the enamel on the pews glisten. Terry was amazed at the black Jesus that hung on the cross in the stained glass windows. The preacher's podium was made of dark mahogany, trimmed in gold and was elevated so that all could see. The church was simply magnificent, breathtaking.

The building could hold over five hundred people easily but was already packed. People sat in chairs lining the middle aisle. There were no additional chairs, the back pews were filled, and Terry was standing by himself in a rear corner. A familiar old lady usher grabbed Terry by the arm and took him to the front of the church; there was a seat on the second row. He was near the armrest, which he didn't mind, but he was also near the front, which was unexpected and bothered him a little bit. Terry could not believe his luck. After a few minutes, it then dawned on him that he would have to stand and introduce himself. That bothered him more than the seating arrangement.

The Ladies Mass Choir entered the sanctuary looking and sounding great. The ladies stepped into that church as though they owned it. Terry was very impressed. His attention went straight to Veronica. She had rhythm and looked like she knew what she was doing. She didn't see him, or she wasn't looking. Even after she was seated, she still didn't see him. She was busy singing. The choir sounded great despite the fact that Terry was not as focused on the singing as much as he was on getting her attention. As they finished their selection, the choir sat down. She still didn't see him.

They had been in service for an hour. She still didn't see him. Veronica decided to get up to go to the rear of the church to the restroom. The familiar old lady usher read the announcements and asked for all visitors to stand and introduce themselves. Terry was one of twelve people. He introduced himself, sat down and noticed that Veronica still did not see him.

He finally stopped looking for her attention when they took up the second offering. Terry was ready to focus on what the preacher had to say. He decided not to look up in the choir until church was over.

Reverend Wilson, a young black preacher, started his sermon with, "What is your purpose for coming to church?" He answered, "Hopefully, to get the message from God and our savior Jesus Christ that will steer you away from sin." Terry was hooked into this sermon from the first question. Terry knew that he had the wrong intentions for coming to church this day. But he was willing to give the Reverend his undivided attention. Veronica became a distant memory.

Reverend Wilson had worked the congregation into a frenzy by the time he got to the crux of the sermon. Then he made a statement that Terry would never forget.

"Now, I don't know what y'all are thinking, but when we get to Heaven, there will be no timeout. There will be no one raising a finger and walking out of Heaven, telling the Lord, 'I gotta go somewhere'.

"When you get to Heaven, you're going to praise Him all day and night. I'll tell you why you should've come to church today. To praise Him. Don't leave here and stop praising him. Once you exit those doors, praise Him all day and all night. Praise Him till the day you die. Praise Him, people. Praise Him."

Reverend Wilson finished his sermon with everyone on his or her feet, applauding his delivery of the word. The church got louder and louder as people shouted, "Thank you, Lord," "Have Mercy", and "Hallelujah." The organist kept playing a rhythm that had folks clapping and hollering. After about two minutes of this praise session, a group of stewards consisting of older men came in front of the Mass Choir to sing a special selection. They started humming. Terry remembered the first few notes from when he was small. The familiar song hit Terry in the middle of his heart. The big, old gray haired man with fifties styled glasses with black trim started with his deep voice. *"At the gate, I know, At the gate I know, At the gate I know, Somebody's waiting at the gate, I know."* The last time Terry heard this song was when Uncle Jesse was singing the lead in St. Paul A.M.E. Church in Georgetown, South Carolina.

The man's male background singers joined him on the second stanza. *Papa will be waiting.* Then the women's mass choir started their part. *Mama, will be waiting.* Terry was so overcome with hearing this song that his right leg started shaking. Every deep note the big man sang vibrated through his entire body. Terry thought about his Uncle Jesse being at the gate and started crying. He couldn't believe what was happening. He had gone almost thirty years without getting the Holy Ghost. Then, all of a sudden, with the dream girl of his life, in front of total strangers, and in front of the church, he did. Terry had given up on stopping the tears, as hard as he tried, he could not stop his legs and body from shaking. The men sang the song for the longest time, and Terry could feel the Lord rushing through his body. Terry jumped up and shouted, "Lord, have mercy," grabbed the pew in front of him with both hands, bowed his head down and started shaking his head from side to side between his arms. His legs still shook and his head stayed down. A lady stood up beside him rubbed his back and wiped the tears from his face. The familiar old lady usher took a paper fan and cooled Terry's face with a constant wave. Terry kept thinking, *Lord, have mercy.*

When the men finished the song, Terry was still standing. Reverend Wilson asked the congregation to stand. They went through the call for discipleship and the benediction. Then the service was over. Terry still shook as he sat down again. Veronica had come from the choir to sit beside him. Terry did not know what happened. He did not care. He just felt so relieved by the experience. Veronica took the place of the women rubbing his back as he sat and cried for a few minutes more. He kept saying, "I'm sorry. I don't know what happened." Veronica kept saying, "Don't worry, Terry, it's going to be alright."

As they drove back to the parking lot, Terry said little.

"Mr. Foster, would you like to get something to eat?"

"No, thanks. I'm going to go home and regroup."

Veronica smiled, gave him her number, and said. "You better call me before I leave."

Terry said "Yeah. Thanks.

Terry was embarrassed to call Veronica back. He concentrated on getting his act together and listening and learning from his screams. But he did think about her every day.

49

Part Three

He Who Loves Least,

Controls the

Relationship

Chapter 9
Queva's World

Terry knew that revisiting the hard times of his past through screaming could make him a stronger person. His eagerness to better himself, coupled with the new insight he found would guide him to his purpose in life. Terry began screaming over the horrible experiences of his life. Queva, a woman he loved unconditionally, was the best starting point. Terry knew that once he understood this relationship, he could help anyone.

She was his Queva! His girl! His lady! They met on campus. Terry sparked her interest by challenging her to dance all night with only him. He knew this would upset any boyfriend or interested suitors. She was beautiful, charming, charismatic. She was a cheerleader and a dancer. Terry first saw her clapping her hands in front of her and stepping to stay on beat. She accepted his challenge, and they danced on again and off again for three years.

Her bubbly attitude made her a true winner in his eyes. Terry loved her more than she could imagine; he should have known that loving her was the wrong way to deal with such an attractive lady. Playing hard to get would have been his best defense.

Looking back, Terry knew that their relationship should have ended years before it did. The thought of Queva and the drama she brought still made Terry shudder. Terry determined that screaming through their experience would strengthen him or drive him into a state of depression, but still he asked, "Why did they have so many problems?"

Terry thought he knew this woman. His admiration for her extended beyond the normal person's concept of love. Vince and so many of his friends would say, "Tee, your butt is whipped." And his grandmother used to say, "Your nose is so wide open, you can't see where you going, child."

Queva and Terry could talk for hours. Terry fell in love with her after their first night. They spent an entire summer together traveling, talking, and walking. His love for her was innocent and infinite. They had a true friendship based on respect and trust.

Queva's ambitions were to be a clone of Jackie Onassis or Princess Diana. She wanted to be loved and liked by the Joneses, the Kennedys and the Smiths. She wanted to be spoiled beyond royalty. She had the looks to demand it, and she had the audacity to use Terry's heart as a stepping stone to grasp it. Queva was the young woman that every man falls for and wants to marry. She had a unique way of creating "Queva's World."

On many occasions, Terry felt sorry for her and treated her like his sister because her objectives were naively skewed. Terry was trying to teach her how to be unselfish. This was a big mistake!

The first time Terry took Queva home to meet his family, they were struck by the apparent way Terry felt for this woman. It was all over his face. "Terry and Queva sitting in the tree, k-i-s-s-i-n-g, first come love, then come marriage then comes Terry with the baby carriage," his little sister and her friends sang while double-dutching near the carport.

Terry's Dad pulled him to the side and said, "Queva seems to be a nice girl, but make sure you know what you are doing before you think about marriage."

Terry laughed and said, "I'm not thinking about marriage!"

The mother smiled when they came through the door saying, "Oh this is the young lady that has Tee's heart in the palm of her hand."

Queva laughed and said, "I think it's the other way around, Mrs. Foster."

The mother hugged Queva and replied, "Well, we're going to have to talk about maintaining the Foster men."

Terry gave his mama a frown, and his dad smirked and said, "Oh Lord! Tee you better keep an eye on those two!" Everyone laughed.

The day spent with his family was one of the proudest moments of their relationship. Terry knew that he had a good, beautiful woman with an equally beautiful spirit by his side. Terry's entire family welcomed her and there appeared to be no negative comments about them as a couple. Queva even felt that she was attending *her* family reunion before the day was over. They met with all his uncles, except Uncle Jesse, his aunts, grandmother and hoards of cousins. Queva even got a chance to see his high school friends.

After they said their good-byes and pulled out of the carport, Queva smiled her biggest smile, then said, "Tee, I love your family. They are so nice! You know you look like your mother and father."

Terry laughed and said, "Everyone thinks I'm their little brother."

"I was really nervous about meeting your mother!"

"I told you there was no reason to worry about my family liking you, especially my mother." Terry started shaking his head as he pulled into a gas station to fill up. He asked her if she needed anything out of the store, and she said, "No, Tee."

As he began to pump gas, Queva got out of the car and walked toward him, looking serious. Astonished, Terry quickly uttered, "What's wrong, baby?" She shook her head, said nothing and took three graceful steps towards him. She grabbed his free hand, placed her other hand around his neck and laid a kiss on him. He felt her joy, her gratification, and her love. As she pulled away she said "I love you, Tee." This kiss was the greatest kiss Terry ever had!

A guy sitting in passenger side of a truck on the other side of their gas pump said, "I've never seen anyone kiss like that. I thought I was in the movies; y'all make a beautiful couple." Queva laughed, and Terry said, "Thanks man." When Terry paid the cashier, she said "That was an amazing kiss; I'm surprised you remembered to pay."

Terry smiled and covered his mouth with his hand, wiping lipstick off of his lips. "I almost forgot!"

Queva and Terry laughed and flirted the entire way back to campus. Terry thought staying close to their families was the best thing for their relationship.

In the fall semester, Queva and Terry had to manage a long distance relationship. That brought major problems. He had to move to work in Arlington, Virginia for a year as part of his internship before graduating. Queva had to stay in school, of course. There was no doubt in his mind that they could make everything work out. The pressures of the long distance relationship grew, but she gave him her word that she wouldn't allow another man to befriend her with the wrong intentions. All of her male friends would know that he was number one. Terry knew he would never cheat on her.

He trusted and believed everything Queva said: "Terry, we went to the movies;" "We are only friends;" or "Tee, Honey, I stayed at Kathy's apartment last night." One day he literally followed her to see if his Queva was telling the truth. The law of the land calls this stalking, but he referred to it as an unauthorized investigative reconnaissance for the heart (UN-IRTH)

They talked every day, and he pretty much knew where she was supposed to be. Terry parked near her apartment, watching her door until the twilight. He then saw her, the love of his life, in someone's arms. She was kissing another man.

Terry put his head on the steering wheel and mumbled, "I knew it, I knew it." He started to get out of his car and confront them together, but his disgust was paralyzing. He stared at the guy's burgundy Chevrolet turning out of the parking lot.

He decided to calm down and hang out with his good friend Kenny until the midday. He was a walking zombie. Terry's heart was crushed to pieces. Kenny knew that Terry was troubled. Kenny didn't bother to even try to make Terry feel better; he just handed him a beer. Terry called her from Kenny's house, leaving a message to expect him in town in three hours. Over the next several hours, he drank, he slept, and he put Queva on trial. She became the defendant, testifying on the witness stand. He became the high-powered prosecutor, the jury, and the judge, placing the pieces into the puzzle.

He entered the house as usual; they kissed, hugged, exchanged miss-yous and surprises. He held his temper and kept his composure like a professional Broadway actor. Terry assumed that she wouldn't tell him the truth because she wanted to keep him as a boyfriend. Or maybe she didn't want to hurt him. Maybe she didn't really like this other guy. Amazingly, Terry was thinking of excuses for her rendezvous. Then it hit him like the Chicago wind in winter—she was in control of every aspect of this relationship. He lived to please her. Terry R. Foster had an uncontrollable love. In other words, he lost his mind and the control of his emotions.

He asked her what she had done the night before and why she hadn't answered the phone.

She answered, "It was a girls' night out. I slept over at Danita's house."

Terry's puzzle was complete. He stood up and said, "Hey, I left something in the car. Let me go get it." He then walked outside, took a big deep breath. He got to his car, cranked it, and left.

It was hard to walk out on the love of his life that day. It was a long, dark trip back home. But he had heard her liar's voice, and things would never be the same.

He opened his eyes after this screaming expedition with a new understanding. Terry's soul came up with this passage in his journal.

Liar's Voice

I heard it, and it always comes around the dirty deed
Now our most important connection bleeds
Then that's why I couldn't sleep last night
Then that's why my stomach was tight
Then that's why my eyes twitched
Making my legs shake, as our bonds of trust unknowingly break
It was a nightmare for me, but am I the villain in your fairy tale?

Obviously,
You don't know how I know your every move
I studied you from the moment we met
In actuality, I was in school

It's not the first time
I have heard a crooked, twisted, hopeful excuse
Leading me away from the total truth
I prayed that I heard it for the last time
I can't deal with love lies; they're too evil for my mind

God gave me the ability to sharpen my hearing
And your liars voice made me lose my bearings
It is amazing how close my ears are to my heart
Because when I heard with my eardrums
My heart instantly fell apart

There's no need to confess now
I knew within a second!
When you had the audacity to tell a lie
That's when I knew what happened
The true trust in this relationship had died a bloody end
Only because I heard the liar's voice from deep within
I'm happy to say, I'm not a glutton for punishment anymore
You have fun with your acquaintance, don't worry
God will walk me to the Door!

Believe it or not, Terry gained control of what they could manage to salvage of the relationship because he did not love Queva in the same capacity. She would come with explanation after explanation but never the truth. She called him numerous times, trying to pacify his crying pride and to repair his shattered image of her. Terry determined that they could be social and even lovers, but they would never marry. Men have memories like elephants; they don't forget, and they crave to trample everything that reminds them of a bad experience. After several months of her begging, Terry decided to reunite with Queva. He wanted to teach her how to love a man like him. This was his form of punishment and revenge. Sadly, Terry needed her in his life until he found someone better. Ironically, he became the selfish being that he had tried to correct. Terry played Queva and any other woman that dared to come near him.

Terry dated many women as he professed continued love to Queva. He did not respect women who expressed an interest in him. He did not love these women. The objectives were sex, money and material things. The fellows said to him, "Give those women the five 'F' treatment, Tee: find them, feed them, fool them, freak them, and forget about them." Tee took their advice to heart.

Terry started remembering the times when Queva caught him with other women. She had been practicing her UN-IRTH techniques. She would approach him in anger and disgust, but she still wanted to be with Terry. There were several issues Queva had to deal with. First, she felt guilty for starting this mess. Second, she knew he was not being the loving Terry Foster she knew. She hoped that once Terry stopped the nonsense of promiscuity, he would be a prime fruit for the marriage basket. Third, Queva enjoyed the defiant attitude and the backbone Terry displayed when she questioned him, and he knew that she wanted him to be in control. Terry had to monitor the way he treated her, never being too nice and being just bad enough to keep her so busy thinking of Terry Foster, that she'd have no time to create her own escapades.

After screaming, Terry wrote about the days when he tried to justify his actions towards Queva and the women who cornered him at his apartment, theaters, and grocery stores and stalked him.

Game Time

Playing in the games of sin
Has no rules
We twirl morality on one finger
And grab temptation with nine

So,
Do you call me trifling?
Do you call me a player?
But maybe you should call your soul a naysayer!
Because you know how to live your life
We should only touch as husband and wife

So,
Don't get upset if I choose other players
And don't direct blame
They tend to be custom-tailored
We attempt to set rules to mock
The true establishment of love
We parade in the devil's den
Devouring his sinful food with plastic gloves
Our behavior can even destroy our health
Just remember you decided to play this game yourself

Now,
I'll apologize if I hurt you in anyway
But I strongly suggest you exit the game today!
Because your spirit likes to be treated in a godly way
You feel pain because your soul hates decay

Now,
Grab your moral book with ten fingers and
Keep it in the palms of your hands
Make temptations hit the grounds
Disappearing in the sands
Remember,
Temptation will resurface
If your moral foundations sway

And if I still play the games of sin
It will cause you to visit the same old painful gates
On a different day

You see
I know what you need
I say the right things
And your lustful thoughts allow sin to clip your wings
And I won't turn you away from my desires
Because I'm even weaker than the players I retire

Now,
If I see your moral foundations are as strong as iron ore
I may try to ride your coattails towards Heaven's doors
Can you understand that I play in the games of sin?
I just haven't found a reason
To help me change from within

Hey,
I will respect you and I will never hurt you
I can tell you the truth about anything
But always remember I play in a game
And if you believe in sex before marriage then
It's always your name that you sign for blame

Understand,
No one wins in the games of sin
Morality should be held by ten fingers and
Temptation should never make you give in

Now! Now!
Don't call me trifling, and don't call me a player!
Check your soul to see if you are a naysayer
There are no rules in this game we play
You just happened to be the play of the day!
Touchdown, home run, and a buzzer winning basket for two
Remember there are no fouls
The decision is on you!

Now,
Are you in the game or
Are you on the sidelines?
Sit in the audience with abstinence on your mind

Because these games of sin are not made for your kind
Better yet, just leave the arena with God on your mind

And make sure to trash that four-leaf clover
And ask God to make sure
Your player's game is over!

Chapter 10
What Makes You Play?

Tee realized that he was deep in the game; he had become evil in his soul and in his spirit. He brought pain like his father brought misery to his mom. He was the Uncle Jesse that Ms. Dee and Ms. Shirley chastised and gossiped about day in and day out.

The sin in which he was engaging was seemingly justifiable, but Terry knew better! Terry tried to fool himself into thinking good results could come out of bad behavior, but he knew that he'd reap what he sowed!

Terry talked with many girlfriends and tried to figure out what made them stay in the game so long. Queva brought a lot of pain and misery to his life, but did it justify the pain and disrespect he was giving to others? No! Terry's mother raised him to respect women.

One of the most important things in his quest to know himself was to find out why he played so long. One day after going to church, he decided to scream. He held the bible in his lap this time. Everything else was as usual: no television, no music, dim lights, his comfortable chair and no shoes. He lay his head back and slowly closed his eyes. Terry tried to think what he liked about the games of sin! He screamed for several hours to find what made him the addict.

Terry had some very good reasons. He liked the novelty of new women. Boredom came regularly. He felt a challenge to see what she had to offer. He'd wait for her to give something that only she could ever give him.

Terry liked the variety, different sizes, complexions, hair, nails and bodies. Terry liked the attention his shallow friends would give him when he had touched a woman that they all wanted!

Vince would say, "You know her! Oh man! She is fine!"

Terry wanted his crew of friends to know that he could play better than many and that he might even be the best they knew! He hoped they would talk about him like a legend! Some people call it peer pressure. Terry called it a twisted form of respect.

Terry wanted the women to pay attention to him because he had flair, because he knew how to entertain. He loved to make smiles! He wanted the women to feel like queens in his presence! He wanted them to advertise that Terry was the man that should be their husband. They would advertise that he was a good man but not ready to settle. The gossip would bring confident women with pizzazz. Many had the ability and the goods to tie the good man down! It even became a challenge for many of his women friends. Terry thought to himself, *I became a younger Uncle Jesse.*

After two hours of screaming, the bible had fallen to his side, and Terry had found the answer to, *What makes you play in the games of sin?* Terry's soul answered with *The Remembrance Game.* This was the feeling Terry had with *every* woman he encountered. He wanted them to remember how he was able to satisfy.

The Remembrance Game

I hope you remember me!
I touched you and sparked a million nerves
I kissed you with the worlds softest lips and
I kept your body's attention three days after
We made pleasurable play with our bellybuttons

I knew you from the start
We were friends within seconds
You laughed, I smiled
I laughed, you smiled

We knew we would play a game
In which there are no losers
If we always remember each other

Are we still winning? Do you remember me?

Oh! How I remember every sound of our passion
Your beautiful walk and that countenance of an angel
To remember touching your body builds pressures in my veins

I remember you in all aspects
You are still a winner
Am I?
Do you remember me?

While his mind and heart caved into passion, lust and temptation, Terry's spirit was always looking for the right woman to take him out of the game. Consequently, women stayed in the game simply because they were hoping for Mr. Right, just as Terry stayed in the game because of his hope to find Ms. Right.

Sometimes couples knew beforehand they were not Mr. and Ms. Right. They still tried to make things happen because of loneliness, but mainly sex was the issue. Enjoying the company and the pleasure of sex was a game of sorts. Many wanted to satisfy and prove to peers that they knew what they are doing. Some relationships ended within hours but each relationship had the same purpose—satisfaction and showcasing attributes.

The game started with one's first real kiss. Remember how you wanted to try your lips on someone to see how it felt, to perfect your technique, and to prove to your counterpart you knew the art of kissing! The main reasons for trying the kiss was to get closer to an admirer and, of course, to prove your physical prowess. You wanted your counterpart to remember the kiss, as well as the time you shared, as being commendable, if not the best. Terry still remembered his first kiss. It was a remembrance game.

Part Four

Strengthening Oneself

Chapter 11
Monumental Shame

The first time Tee came across racism was probably the worst time in his life. Tee was eight years old, adventurous, and happy beyond content, especially when he spent time with his friends Patrick and Shaun. Dre made the gang complete. They were inseparable. They managed to develop a tremendous friendship that has lasted over twenty-three years.

There was not much for young boys to do while growing up in rural South Carolina. The boys always managed to stay out of trouble, mainly by not getting caught. Their bicycles were like cars. They'd ride for miles a day, talking, throwing rocks, and exploring the pine-oak laden countryside of Georgetown County.

On this particular day, the boys decided to go to Vat Road, a well known place in the community where people dumped trash and old furniture. They'd search for bottles, find them, and line them up for execution. Their parents hated for them to hang around Vat Road. The old man would say, "Y'all gonna find more than just bottles in that dump." Well, that was an invitation for them to live on Vat Road. If they could find anything exciting, it was better than hanging around the front yard.

One day while doing their bottle hunt, the boys found blood and globs of flesh in a fire trail right beside the dump. The smell was unbelievably horrible. Pat and Dre, the oldest, were the first ones to discover the remains. Shaun and Terry were less than eager to get closer. Shaun kept saying, "Oh man, we found a body!"

Shaun and Terry followed Pat and Dre further into the forest. Then the boys found a great mass of guts. They couldn't tell if it was from a human. At that moment, they realized that they might be in danger. Pat said, "Oh hell, I'm getting out of here." They ran back toward their bikes as hard and as fast as they could. They had to get home!

When they finally got to the dirt road, shots rang out. POW! POW!

Everyone ran for cover, hiding behind trash piles, old rusted washers, and barrel and tire piles. Then to their astonishment, two trucks full of white men came up Vat Road, driving slowly. As Terry peeped from behind the rusted end of a barrel, he saw the men getting closer. It was at that point that the boys could hear each other breathing. Pat kept saying, "SHHH! SHHH! Don't move!" Dre and Shaun were hiding behind the old rusted washers, and Pat was adjacent to the barrel, lying flat beside a pile of roof shingles and tires.

The trucks came by slowly, and they could hear the men laughing and talking, country music blasting. It seemed like an eternity. The first truck passed, but the second truck stopped right in front of our hideout. One man said, "Whew, you smell dem deer guts!"

At this point, Terry was so afraid that he started trembling. The tension was so great that it was unbearable. Terry didn't want to blow their cover with his trembling. And just as Terry prayed to concentrate on staying still, Dre's nerves got the best of him. Dre jumped up and said, "Oh Lawd, they got us!" The four white men looked at him as though he was crazy. Pat and Shaun got up as though they were caught. Terry slowly arose and immediately headed towards the bikes, which had been lying in some bushes less than thirty feet from them. Terry just knew that those men were going to kill them.

The white man driving the truck laughed and said, "Y'all niggers getting high on dem deer guts? Y'all better get off of this road before you end up like that deer!" Before the man got all the words out of his mouth, Terry had mounted his bike and peddled all the way home. The rest of the gang did the same.

The first time Terry came across racism, someone called him nigger and threatened his life. Terry thought, *I must have felt only a fraction of what a runaway slave felt.* This was terrible. But until this day, the boys still teased Dre about blowing their cover.

Dre's remark never changed, "Hell, I thought we were going to get killed."

A few months later, "Let's burn that sucker down," Pat called out in response to a combination of harsh run-ins with the rednecks in the area. It was one of the first devilish acts the boys thought about doing to correct many years of wrongs. Terry had no trouble justifying it. That day, although over twenty years ago, still stood out in his mind. They were going to burn down Hangman Tree, which ironically was within a mile of Vat Road.

He could still feel his feet hitting the pavement on his march to bring justice to the blacks in the community. Terry can remember asking his grandfather, grandmother, mother and father about that tree, and they all gave the same story:

That's the old tree where they use to hang colored and slaves, where the Klan use to have rallies and picnics. They decided to make it a landmark. It was a good day when a big eighteen wheeler came down that highway and knocked that limb off of that tree. That serves them folks right for praising that old tree. I wished I hada uprooted the whole thing.

The old water oak tree had a perfect limb, which served as the executioner for many blacks during slavery time and the uncivilized era after the slaves were free. The tree was between two hundred and two hundred fifty years of age in 1977 when Terry and his crew set out to end its long time existence. By the time they set out on their escapade, this tree, ugly due to the injury it sustained in the 60s, had grown to a diameter of around four-and-a-half feet at breast height. The whites in town placed a metal barricade around it so errant cars would not damage the trunk. Terry even thought rednecks redirected Highway 17 to save this tree's life.

This mission was an act of responsibility that Terry and his friends conjured up to pay back black people. Dre said, "We have to take a chunk out of it." Pat was simply upset because the old white man that owned the store spat a wad of tobacco juice at him, barely missing his bicycle tire. Pat and Dre were also upset because these boys that they knew from elementary school said, "Our dads are rednecks, and we don't like niggers!"

"We beat those crackers' butt!" Pat said. Pat and one white boy were suspended from school for one day for fighting.

The principal told Pat's mom, "Pat knocked the boy's tooth out; he deserves to be suspended." Pat's mom understood. Terry thought his Dad was going to whip Dre to death, but his Dad said, "Serve your time in detention and no more fighting or name calling!" Pat and Dre became heroes for the black teachers and a target for the white teachers. The white teachers started asking them more questions than ever. Dre, being the intellect of the two, had no problems. However, Dre had to make Pat get ready for the questions. Dre decided that everyone would study together as a gang before any one touched a TV, basketball or bike. Dre and Pat found a lot of pride in defeating the teachers.

That day Pat kept saying, "Just think of all the black people that hung by the rope on this tree. Every time one of those crackers drives by, they smile because they know that this tree scared the black folk."

The crew began the mission to make the infamous tree a pile of ashes. Pat and Terry brought mayonnaise bottles topped off with gasoline. Dre had the matches. Shaun ran north to watch out for cars. During this time Dre had managed to scale the tree. Dre reached the hole on the tree's stem where the hangman's limb once protruded over the highway.

Terry handed Pat his mayonnaise bottle and ran to the south end to watch out for cars. There were none, as luck would have it.

Pat tied the mayonnaise bottle to a string of twine that was attached to Dre's belt loop. Dre pulled the bottle up and began pouring the gas on the inside of the heart of the tree and around the sides of the tree. Pat had kicked a circle around the tree to prevent the fire from jumping into the nearby woods. Luckily, it was a dry, hot, windless day. Pat opened the second bottle and poured the gas on the tree's roots and trunk.

Then all of a sudden, Shaun let out a yell, "Hey! Hey!" He could hear the car coming. Dre jumped from about twelve feet up and landed in the arms of Pat. Everyone disappeared into the woods.

When the car passed and the sight was clear, Pat and Dre lit the tree. Within seconds, the gas was aflame and the tree was burning. Since everyone had to come to Terry's end, he had a chance to watch that tree burn the longest. A beautiful black smoke came from the tree as if black spirits were being released, racing to heaven.

They ran home to change clothes and to get on bikes, so they could ride as far away from the tree as possible. Everyone had nervousness in their steps and actions because they knew they had done wrong. This criminal act could have put the crew in detention, jail, prison. It could even have gotten them murdered by the Klan.

Later on that night, the old man and mother entered Terry and Dre's room. Dre looked at Terry as if to say, *Don't even think about telling the truth.*

The old man did all the talking, "Dre, Terry, I know that you boys know better than starting fires. Don't you?"

The two replied, "Yes sir!"

"Well, somebody set old Hangman tree on fire today. I want to know if y'all did it."

Dre said, "We were on Drexler Road all day, Daddy."

Terry said a reassuring, "All day."

Daddy said, "Well, okay, don't let me find out y'all lied to me."

The next day, it was in the local county paper, "Monument Scarred by Arsonist." It went on to say that no one was caught and that the fire was extinguished after damage was done to the bark of the tree. However, the tree still stood.

Afterwards, Pat, Shaun, Dre and Tee swore never to do anything that would get them in jail ever again. They didn't do enough damage to the tree. Some branches caught on fire but fluttered out because the tree was too green with life. They only scarred the tree black once the gas burned off.

Looking back on his delinquency, Terry realized that he had a small victory. In the course of the mission, they risked their freedom. They could have burned down surrounding communities. The crew rehashed horrifying memories for blacks and made whites rejoice about the tree's resistance to death.

Uncle Jesse came home three weeks after the dastardly mission. Pat, Dre, Shaun and Terry were all hanging around the front stoop of the house, fixing bikes. Uncle Jesse and Dad drove up in the carport. They stopped by to talk to the boys. Uncle Jesse asked a point blank question, "Did y'all boys try to fire up that old Hangman tree up the road?"

They all laughed and said almost in harmony, "No, Sir!"

Then Uncle Jesse and the old man laughed. As they went through the front door, the crew just snickered with laughter. Pat said, "I wish I had a torch and more gas." They laughed even louder. Seconds after Pat's comments, to everyone's surprise, the front door opened again. The boys were in complete shock. They wondered if anybody heard their remarks. Uncle Jesse stuck his head and half of his body out to talk to the boys. He said, "Fellows, y'all need to keep that laughing and comments like that down!" He paused.

"And make sure y'all keep them secrets to yourself! Just like me and my brother keeps our secrets."

The boys looked at him puzzled, and then he said with a smile, "Who do y'all think was driving that eighteen wheeler that broke off the limb of Hangman tree?"

Terry and Dre's dad popped his head beside Uncle Jesse and smiled as though they were taking a photo.

Then Uncle Jesse said, "I hope I'm alive when someone finally uproots that old tree." They all laughed!

That tree still stands and its amazing how that tree could be considered a monument. Not long ago, Pat, now the state senator, pledged to Dre, Shaun, and Terry, that he would finally get a legal chance to up-root Hangman tree. One day, all the black spirits can be released from that tree. One day, judgement will come.

Chapter 12
River

Terry worked late to prepare for the upcoming week. When he finished, stressed by the day's occurrences, He decided to relieve his anxieties. Terry sat behind his desk and began screaming. He wrote this story in his journal.

The sun had just settled in the west, around five-thirty in the afternoon. The moon was on its way, but because of the clouds, it would be sometime before anyone could see its full beauty. The temperature was just cold enough to keep the lovers from their nightly stroll, just right for curling up under a quilt. The line of sight was less than forty yards, and the night had a breeze strong enough to rustle the leaves.

This is the night, Hank said to himself. He had been thinking about this day for the last eleven years. It was November 23, 1820. It was the best time to run away.

The first step over the barbed fence was so loud that he thought the Dawsons could hear him at the dinner table. It was his first step to freedom, dead or alive. He had passed the point of no return. His senses heightened to protect him from danger. His second step was a tiptoe.

As he increased his steps, he fell into a rhythm. Footsteps to freedom made comforting music.

Hank knew that his life depended on the first two days. Hank concentrated on every step he took, never looking behind but always listening for everything— a squirrel's shuffle, a lizards scrawl, even the crickets' chirp. Hank would say quick prayers as he kept running: Lawd, don't let that be a white man. Whew! Thank you!

Before it was over, his journey would become a continuous prayer and praise session to God. Every step closer to freedom brought new praise.

Hank's heart was pounding against his ribs, making his body tremble with awareness. Freezing fear filled his lungs. North was the destination, and, as one freed slave would say, "If you can get past da river, then you can get to the North." The river was the recurring thought in his mind, but Hank's first goal was to get to the road that would get him to the river.

Hank remembered when he and his mother entered this area. It had the pretty rocks along the sides, and they sparkled when the sun hit them just right. Hank figured they were there to keep the roads from washing away in high water. Hank knew that once he reached that point, he was within twenty miles of the river.

A blanket, thirty pieces of potatoes and stolen bread from the kitchen would be the meal and bed for at least two weeks. Hank knew that the chase would begin anywhere from eight to sixteen hours after his escape. As he ran toward the midnight, his thighs were burning with fatigue. Thorns and branches scratched Hank's face and chilled hands as night ventured towards morning.

Hank gauged himself to run fast for twenty minutes then to rest for three minutes. He would take a big break at midnight: ten to fifteen minutes, then back to freedom's trail. Hank ran twenty-six miles through gradual sloping oak and pine forested areas and occasional heavy brush with briars. Hank tried to cross these areas with caution. He thought, *These briars gonna kill me before Master can!* as he plucked thorns from his hand.

Hank was a muscular slave with brown eyes, black skin, and a no-smile demeanor. He stood six feet tall and weighed about one hundred ninety pounds.

Hank barely knew his father. He could only remember a hand like his picking him up time after time when he was young. The old folk said his father, Joecum, had a hearty laugh very similar to Hank's. His mom told him that Joecum was sold when he was five.

This was not Hank's first time running away. He and his mom tried running when he was seven. Hank was going to be sold. The other slaves said, "She was still thinking they were running freedom's trail. She never got her mind right!" Thirteen days after the runaway attempt, she was freed into Heaven. Hank wore a good whipping. Pity was given to him after twelve hits. He watched, heard, and felt his mother take hit after hit after hit after hit. She had about twenty-two lashes. She stopped crying. She only bled. They whipped her unconscious. She died from infections caused by the beating. Before she died, she whispered to Hank, "Get to da river, pray de whole time, and you'll be free!" Hank never forgot. Hank never forgot.

The sale didn't go through because the goods were damaged and a runaway threat. Hank would say, "If she hada lived, then we woulda been together longer." The old folk could only shake their heads.

Hank passed the point where the posse caught his mama and him. He remembered her cry, "Run baby!" She tried to hold them off, but dog bites were too harsh. The head overseer on a big, beautiful black horse caught Hank.

Not this time, not this time, overseer! Hank said to himself. Hank did not slow down during this span of the escape. He even skipped his break and ran for an entire hour!

77

Hank would mumble every time he thought of his mother, "I'm gonna be free! Reda's boy gonna be free!"

After about forty miles of traveling, Hank's body became exhausted. Hands swollen with cold, scratched cheeks and aching thighs made him take a needed rest. The desire to go on burned his mind, but his body could not follow. An old oak tree became the spot for rest. Hank sat at the base of the tree facing freedom. He unraveled his rations and bit into a cold potato. The blanket covered his head and feet, attempting to conceal him. Hank said a prayer, asking God to awaken him with freedom and not the overseer's horse. After almost a half-hour of sleep, one eye opened to darkness. *That's good,* thought Hank, *I didn't oversleep!* Hank wrapped the rations and was up and running again. There were about two hours before any daylight and there was no barking. Hank thought, *That's good too!*

Hank knew the reaction back at the plantation. Slaves would be called around four-thirty in the morning with knocks at the doors, dogs barking and a scratchy voice hollering, "Let's go! Get up!" The slaves in Hank's shack, an old man with six boys—all orphans generally did the early morning work. Feeding the hogs, chicken, horses and other livestock were the main chores. There were no problems getting this shack up, and the chores were seldom checked. Hank knew the problem would come around six o'clock when Parks, the head overseer, would gather every slave for fieldwork. Sometimes he'd count, sometimes he'd oversleep, and sometimes he'd forget. That day, Parks counted, and he came up short.

The posse separated into two teams, one of dogs with trailers through the woodlands, and the other was the road team for the town and communities nearby. Seven men with horses and six bloodhounds were on the hunt. Parks knew that Hank had a good head start, and they figured he was heading north towards the river. "All of dem run north!" Parks said with a grimace. "Let's catch this boy and show 'em!"

The river was almost two days by horse from the plantation. Park figured he'd go to the river road and patrol the area while three men hunted in the woods and three others got word to the towns and neighbors.

"He's worth one thousand dollars, let's get em!" screamed Parks. The chase was on. The posse had to overcome at least a thirteen-hour start.

Dawson's slaves enjoyed talking about Hank. Some prayed for him. Others were dreading seeing him get the whip. Some were dreading the overseer's revenge if he got to freedom!

Hank felt the chase. He said to himself, *No need to think luck goin' to come my way! They know I'm gone!* Hank had traveled over sixty miles before he got to the swamp area. It was still dark, but daylight was quickly approaching. The swamp was terrible with green briar patches, mud, and a cold rainy mist. Hank was venturing into the worst part of his travel. Hank took about twenty minutes to get through a one hundred-foot stretch of briars. A shoe was left behind, stuck in mud, because the briars were too painful to re-navigate. It was too dark to find the shoe; there was no time to waste, and the rain was so thick, he couldn't see.

Before morning's end and fifteen miles of swampland, Hank knew he had conquered the biggest threat during this first day. Hank welcomed sunshine as the morning clouds disappeared. The warmth of the sun brought life back into the frozen left foot that wore a tattered piece of blanket, as its shoe. After running for nine miles with few breaks, Hanks body gave in to exhaustion. He slept for two hours by a boulder facing the sun. His entire body was warm! The evening was quickly approaching; the prime time for running was here again. Knowing that he was twelve hours ahead of the posse was not comforting, and it seemed impossible that a man could truly run away from

Dawson's Plantation. "I'm gonna be free, or they gonna kill me," Hank whispered to himself.

Hank knew that when he heard barking, he had to be near the river, or he would die. Hank finished the potato he started biting the day before and took a big bite of the bread. He decided to wait until evening because white men like to hunt during the day. He found a new hiding spot and rested for another hour.

The oak leaves rustling under his feet sounded like thunder. Hank began running on the grassy areas and edges. The prayers kept coming past his lips. The thighs were in desperate need of rest, but there was no time to worry about this pain. The only worry had to be his foot; it was beginning to swell and was very cold. "Lord, I'll be fine." Hank said out loud.

The second day's terrain was better for running. Hank managed to stay out of the night watchmen's view after crossing some roads and sneaking past a few large plantations. As he passed one plantation, he noticed slaves celebrating by a large fire. He knelt, hiding behind a chestnut oak. Hank sighed, and a lonely feeling filled his soul. Hank realized that he had left the only family he ever had. He prayed for friends and a family in the North. His mental picture of the North was heavenly. A silly urge to warm his foot near embers made him turn away and trek on north. "God, I'll be fine," he said.

The bloodhounds and the posse were hot on his trail. The gap of time closed drastically to seven hours. The dogs found the greenbrier patch to be both painful and rewarding. They dug the shoe out of the mud. Their howling turned to screeches as the briars pulled fur and blood. The men traveled two miles out of the way to avoid the briar patch against their horses. One of the horsemen said, "He'll die from bleeding before we catch him."

Hank could feel the river calling him. He kept on trudging, looking for the road with the pretty rocks. Almost two days of travel and Hank's body began slowing down to a couple of miles per hour. It was midnight with a full moon and clear skies. He looked at the stars and smiled. He looked north and saw a sparkle on the ground. He thought immediately, *The road to the river.* He sprinted to the sparkle only to see fireflies. He stopped and gathered his breath and began to cry. Then he laughed and said to himself, *The next time Reda's Boy thinks he sees the road, believe you me, he gonna take his time caus' Dawson's boys might be watching!* He laughed again, thinking, *Even a fool's freedom feels good.*

In the meantime, several dogs were released from their chains. The other dogs were used to guide the posse after a few hours of rest. Parks decided to ride non-stop to the road. He was able to get to the bridge and patrolled a five-mile stretch from one stance.

The morning dew left a direct trail to Hank. He sighed as he entered the grassy area. He figured this would be the doom. Hank decided to look down in the brush, and to his surprise, a malnourished puppy— about seven weeks old—stood beside his feet. The puppy's faint howling and eyes mirrored what was in Hank's soul. Within a second, the puppy was in his arms.

As the fortieth hour of running came to an end, the intensity of the journey changed drastically. Hanks legs, feet, body and soul were fatigued. His appendages dragged with cramps and spasms. Only sheer will fueled his body. Within twenty paces after finding the puppy, Hank found the mother's body, decaying and foul, in heavy brush. His left foot stepped on the rotting carcass, and his right foot tripped over the thick grass and her legs. Hank shook his head in dismay as he fell to the ground, holding the pup with both hands in the air. Hank wondered how the puppy survived. There were no other pups or any plantations within miles. When he picked the pup from the ground, he thought he heard the river and smelled its shoreline. Hank felt new life with this creature. Being fond of the stranded puppy, he decided to name him River. If, by chance, he never made it to the original river, he at least had found one river on freedom's path.

Hank said, "Don't worry, River; things gonna be fine." He rolled away from the carcass and started running again.

After traveling through the tall brush with water oaks, sweet gums and tulip poplars adjacent to the grassy area, Hank saw the morning sun bring the glitter of the river road. The rocks were beautiful to Hank. Within seconds of finding his treasure, Hank heard a horse's trot. He quickly fell to his belly dropping the puppy to his side and the potatoes and blanket under his chest. The line of sight through branches, twigs and grasses revealed another beautiful black horse carrying Parks. Hank sighed internally and prayed for help. He turned on his back to look to Heaven. He thanked the fireflies because they taught him a lesson. Buzzards were circling for River's mother. This sign of death made Hank feel defeated, but he kept his faith.

The posse caught up with the released hounds' barking as though they captured the slave. The dogs mistakenly had circled the decaying body of River's mother. A posse member cursed and screamed with disappointment, "These blasted mutts picked up some dead dog in heat! That nigger might have never come this way. Let's go up to the river road, then come back this way. Let's see if Parks got there yet. Keep them eyes open."

Parks turned his back to the bridge and peered for any movement along the road. Hank figured he would wait until dark or wait until a wagon came by. Both options were risky. If he waited, the bloodhounds could find him from behind. If a wagon came by, he stood the chance of being caught by the wagon owner or the wagon's being searched by Parks at the start of the bridge.

All of a sudden, a big movement in the grassy areas rattled sixty or more quail into flustered flight about a quarter of a mile from where Parks stood. Parks immediately scanned the area as he galloped to the disturbance, gun in hand and ready to shoot. The culprit was River. Parks had an eye on River's head and was ready to fire. Hank took advantage and crossed the road with lightening speed, leaving one footprint in the middle of the dirt road. Relieved, he slowly scampered toward the river.

Parks noticed the malnourished puppy chasing everything that moved. The overseer picked River up and went back to his original stance. He sat River down by his horse and waited for Hank to appear. Within seconds, River picked up Hank's scent mixed with his mother's scent and went after him.

Parks paid the puppy's movement little attention.

The posse made it to Parks and explained the situation. The dogs started barking and scrambling over the one footprint that was left by Hank. They headed into the woods exactly where River had traveled. Parks hollered, "Those damn dogs are now chasing a wild pup that I came across. We need to track back through this area. Those dogs must have lost the scent a couple of miles back. We'll just search until the morning."

Hank came to the the river. He peeped over the tall marshland grass to see if he could see the posse. Without a doubt, he could see some movement near the bridge. Nightfall was near, and the low tide would be coming soon. He had two options— to wait the posse out and cross the bridge after they left or to trudge on up the river to get to a shallow crossing. Hank decided to trek on north along the river looking for an area to cross. He wanted to get as far away from Parks as possible. He thought, *No way I'm gonna to take steps back towards Dawson's plantation, and no way I'm gonna wait! I'll stay on the river!* He laughed. Shortly thereafter, River caught up with Hank. Hank held River in his arms and said, "Not this time, not this time, overseer! I'm goin' to be free! Reda's boy gonna be free just like the river!"

It would be two days of traveling at a moderate pace and twenty degree nights. River would cuddle around Hank's left foot and make it the warmest part of Hank's body. Hank's fondness turned into love for the pup.

Parks and the distraught posse came upon the Dawson's Plantation. Their noisy dogs still barked and howled.

Mr. Dawson came out of the big house anxious and happy, shouting, "Tie him up, dammit! He cost me four days of work. One bad apple spoils the..." Dawson stopped in mid-sentence then said, "He better be dead, Parks!"

Parks made no attempt to say Hank escaped. Parks just shook his head from side to side. Dawson cursed and said, "Well, we gotta teach somebody a lesson!"

They made an example of everyone in Hank's shack. They were beaten and kicked as though they planned the escape. The old man in charge of the boys took ten lashes from the whip; the boys took five.

As the women cured the men's wounds with water and lard, the old man told the slaves to gather around. He said "I'd take more lashes if all y'all could get ta freedom; I done healed from that whip many times." He took a deep breath and continued, "I'll heal better if I'm hit because of freedom. I ain't ever gonna see freedom with these old eyes, but I'll see freedom through Hank's eyes. They can't whip them eyes shut. They can't kick 'em. They can't shoot 'em shut! So y'all be happy for Reda's boy and be happiest 'cause we healing for freedom sake!"

As Terry came out of the screaming expedition, he kept hearing the phone ring. He snapped out of screaming and answered. It was his mother.

Chapter 13
The Unexpected Expected

Terry had seen many friends succeed without their fathers. The sheer will to survive gave many a reason. Others wanted to prove their existence had a purpose. It was never easy on the mother, the grandparents, or aunts, but there were many success stories. Terry figured that faith in God and discipline were the backbone of these successful single parent families.

Joe Foster, appreciated the simple things in life more than Uncle Jesse did. Joe loved his family like Uncle Jesse loved his friends, money, women, and cars. Terry liked to call his dad, Joe Foster, the old man. He was a truck driver with a local route. Joe was going to retire at the end of the year. He put in twenty-five years with this company and was ready to call it quits. He was going back to school to finish his degree. Joe was also anxious to start a satellite office for Uncle Jesse's investment company.

Joe and Uncle Jesse were cut from the same mold. Both men were over six feet tall, muscular and very intimidating, especially when they didn't smile. Dad was fifty and Uncle Jesse was forty eight.

Uncle Jesse's investment company had become very successful in the last five years. After many years of poor returns, the company had finally started making double the profits. Uncle Jesse attributed this increase to his new outlook on business: God first. The old man was anxious to be a part of the business. Their plan to run a satellite office was almost finalized. The old man loved the idea of working for himself.

Every time Uncle Jesse came to visit, he and the old man would get in one of Uncle Jesse's new cars. Uncle Jesse had cars ranging from a lily white Cadillac to a big black Mercedes Benz to an emerald green Jaguar to a candy red Range Rover. They would cruise through the neighborhood bars and stay out late.

The old man got home early from work to avoid Mama's hassle. Uncle Jesse came to the back door and in a blink of an eye, the twosome was cruising in the 1996 Benz with dark tinted windows.

At one o'clock in the morning they were headed home from visiting a family friend. County policemen pulled them over to find out why two black men were driving a luxury car with out-of-state-tags. They ran the tags and then asked Uncle Jesse to step out of the car. They went to give him the sobriety exam and before he knew it, the cop took a nightstick and slapped Uncle Jesse in the back of the head. Uncle Jesse fell down. As he struggled to get to his feet, the cop took the nightstick and fired another blow to the back of his head. Uncle Jesse died instantly. Terry's Dad burst out of the car, horrified. He ran straight into the wooded area adjacent to a small community.

The cop said, "Damn! Get him!" *Pow! Pow! Pow! Pow! Pow!* They fired at him five times. One bullet entered his left shoulder. The old man kept on running. The old man was familiar with this area. He knew he could get onto Taylorsville Road and be a half of a mile from Mr. Frank's house. Mr. Frank was a rich white man who treated Joe and Jesse Foster like brothers. Joe knew that Frank would help him.

Terry's dad ran as hard as he could, holding to his shoulder tight so he wouldn't bleed to death. He could still see the flashing lights. The old man was petrified and weak. He'd lean up against a tree to listen for the officers footsteps and for a quick breather. Blackness surrounded him. He could only see the tops of the trees. He was breathing heavy, huffing and puffing like a wild animal. There had to be at least one cop behind him crouching down on the leaves. The old man couldn't tell if the blue lights were still flashing or if it was locked in his mind. The old man took one final rest near a oak tree before he got on Taylorsville Road. Just as he laid his head back, *Pow!* again. The cop fired, hitting the tree an inch above the old man's head.

Joe scampered the rest of the way like a wounded dog. He aimed straight for Frank's house. He ran into the small ditch near the road. He started running as hard as he could. He saw lights near Frank's house. He thought, *Please be home, Frank.* Joe ran through three yards to get to the big house with white columns in front. Dogs barked and motion sensitive lights came on. Joe made it to the Frank's front door and pressed the doorbell, looking backwards to see if the cop was on his way. Joe pressed and pressed, but there was no movement in the house. He could hear the officer's boots scrape the asphalt. Then Joe saw the officer's shiny badge. The officer was on the walkway. "Come on nigger. Time to go." Dad reached to ring the doorbell one more time. The pistol cocked. "I'll blow your damn head off." Dad just lost hope and fell to the welcome mat. He laid there in blood fearing for his life. The cop got about five feet away and pointed the pistol to the old man's head.

The shotgun barrel came out of the door. "Now Mr. Officer, you can put that gun down. Or I'll have to test this shotgun me and this man used to hunt with thirty some odd years ago." The barrel shook a little bit. "My arm is getting tired, and as far as I can see you are on private property. I know this man. He ain't going to cause no more harm. If you don't move, I'll test that vest you got on."

"This is a police matter, Sir. This nigger ran from a check point."

"Honey," Mrs. Frank yelled from a distant room. "I've got the mayor on the other line, and the sheriff is coming over."

"Boy, if you don't get your ass off of my porch, then I'll unload this here shot gun. You've got five seconds."

"This is a police matter!"

"One! Two! Three!"

"Okay, Okay!"

Mr. Frank pulled his bloody friend into the house. "They beating up Jesse, Frank, they beating up Jesse on McIntosh Road." Frank decided to go outside. The cop had disappeared. The sheriff and a dozen cars pulled up to the house.

The cops came to the door, "Everybody all right?

"No! Get an ambulance for this man."

87

The ambulance and mayor soon followed, but it was too late. Jesse lay dead where his brother had left him on McIntosh Road.

For almost an entire week prior to the encounter with the law, Terry kept having morbid thoughts as though something was about to happen. He knew he was not psychic because God doesn't like psychics. When these thoughts crossed his mind, he'd dismiss them as nonsense or ask God to watch over his family and loved ones.

His mama called him at work when he was writing the passage, *River*. She said with a scratchy voice, "Tee, baby."

Terry knew immediately that something was wrong. He replied, "What's wrong, Ma?"

"Tee, your Uncle Jesse died last night on his way home."

He quickly replied, "What? How, Ma?"

"Baby, your dad is in the hospital, too. They had a rough night."

Tee replied, "What!"

"Dre and Patsy are on their way home."

Tee said, "I'll be there by tomorrow afternoon."

As Terry was flying from Raleigh to Myrtle Beach, he had an excruciating headache from the cabin pressure on the plane. He realized that the expected unexpected happened. Tee never dealt with death very well. Simply, Terry feared death. His mama used to say, "If your friends believe in the word, then death should be joyful because they went to a better place." At a young age, Terry decided that if he enjoyed their company down here, then he would really have a good old time in Heaven. Terry requested aspirin from the flight attendant.

Uncle Jesse and Tee never talked much about church. He'd always ask us, "Whatcha learn in Sunday school?" Terry remembered him sitting in the back of church wearing nice suits. It seemed as though all the women had their eyes on Uncle Jesse and his friends. Terry always liked for Uncle Jesse to let him sit by him in church. It was a more relaxed feeling being away from his parent's backhand slap, pinching of the ears, or ice cold stares when he was misbehaving.

If a few months went by without a phone call, Dad would call Uncle Jesse saying, "Somebody must be whipped and ready to get married." They never missed a beat. Uncle Jesse would reply in the only way he could, "I'm single forever."

Terry had seen many lives end. As he got older, more people succumbed to death. Every experience touched him differently, but always that lost feeling remained.

Tee thought about Uncle Jesse and tried to understand the concept of death. There had to be more than that lost feeling. All he really knew about death was his hatred for funerals and getting the news. It took him several years before he could scream about Uncle Jesse's death. Afterwards, Terry had a better understanding about death. He finally had an answer to the madness surrounding Uncle Jesse's death, but his life was never the same. The journal entry had the following passage. On the opposite page, Terry glued Uncle Jesse's obituary. The single most pivotal point in Terry's life came shortly after he screamed and entered, *Angels Bring the Comfort Down*. Tee's life was never the same.

Angels Bring the Comfort Down

Tears open wounds deep
Gray days carry solemn hints
Those fickle minds gather soon
Faint memories salt the wound

Angels fly through midnight skies
Touching all for dreams this night
Futures revealed by signals you know
Hard to explain your knowledge before

Angels bring the comfort down
Prepares the spirit for softer grounds
Worry none of kites afloat
Flying to Heaven's front door

News reports bring fleshly results
Tears race for grounds in doubt
Gloomy faces stretch through all lines
Tears make the cheeks shine

But the comforter readied your spirit though
So tears of joy would hit the floor
Angels bring the comfort down
Prepares your spirit for softer grounds

Dre and Terry were pretty much like twins; they were both well equipped when things were going well, but they didn't learn from their mistakes. Terry was pleased to know that Dre confided in him when problems occurred. But this time, when Dre ran into personal problems, Terry thought he could not help Dre. Uncle Jesse's murder affected Dre in a devastating way. Dre drank more, smoked cigarettes, and began hating white people and became more violent.

Terry accomplished a great feat by developing a unique understanding of death, but Terry still had to deal with minor pitfalls in life. Terry remembered sad things in his life—humiliation, ignorance, and accidents. He read this passage from his scream every time he came across a pitfall. It helped Terry to strengthen his spirit. Every time something happened, he reviewed the journal entry. It gave him peace of mind and put his problems in a proper perspective. It almost became a remedy for mental, emotional, and physical ailments.

Dre picked up his bible hoping for divine intervention. God would help him, but then Dre would let anger and frustration and depression resurface. Terry gave him the following passage to read because Dre became fed up with people's advice. Dre was never the reading type, but when all chaos erupted, he later told Terry, he continuously read and recited the poem. Dre found that he was no longer angered about Uncle Jesse's death. It became, as he called it, his picker-upper poem. Dre stopped drinking excessively, smoking, and he even tried to forgive white people.

Inspiration # 10   June 28, 1986

When Did Your Leaves Hit the Ground?

Life is like a seed
With luck, you land in the right spot
We are evergreens, oaks, bushes all
Subject to heart-rot

When did your leaf hit the ground?
Did you cry? Did you frown?
Did you take His name in vain?
Or did you realize
He controls your gains?

Every leaf that falls has a purpose and a sound
Did you learn from the fall?
Did you hear His message at all?
Did your leaf carry a seed?
Did it survive through the weeds?
Did you stand tall?
Did you answer His call at all?

When all your leaves touch the ground
And your roots can no longer hold the pounds
Remember the lessons from your leaves and seeds first down
Then you will be blessed before you or a loved one
And death are found

Now, when did your leaf hit the ground?

Chapter 14
Veronica's Daydream

Terry was upset, out of touch, and lonely. The only person he wanted to be with was Veronica. He hadn't called her in two months. He dialed her number in Washington, DC and got a busy signal.

He knew that he should have returned at least one of her calls. He called her later on that night. She answered the phone.

"Hello."

"Hi. Veronica, please?"

"This is she."

"This is Terry."

"Oh! You would call now. When I have my first date in two months waiting in my living room."

"I should have called earlier." Terry replied.

"I'm sorry you didn't."

"Hey, I've been thinking about you the entire time. Hopefully, you'll find the strength and faith to forgive me for not calling. I was embarrassed about what happened at church."

"I knew you probably felt that way. That's why I called you once, but for some reason you didn't return my call.

Something told me you thought I would tease you. I never will tease you about the Holy Ghost. Terry, that's between you and God."

"Veronica, I also had to straighten up my life. If you don't forgive me, I'm hoping you will find the loneliness to be mutually unbearable."

"Ah! Don't try to sweet talk me, Terry."

"I'm not trying…, the reason I called you is because I experienced one of the best events in my life with you."

"Give me a break!" she said out loud. Then she whispered to conceal her phone call from her date, "Give me a break, Terry. You must have a girlfriend or someone special. That's why you didn't call."

"No. That's not it. I've been working long hours, and I've been thinking about my life and you."

"Prove it. You barely know me."

Terry was quick on his feet. He said, "If I can prove that I have been thinking about you, then you will tell that date to go home because something came up?"

"Oh yeah, Mr. Foster, ruin my date. I'll take you up on that. If you can't prove it, then you have to wash my car every time I'm in Raleigh and take me to expensive restaurants. I'll be the judge on whether you win or lose."

"It's a deal, Veronica." Terry said.

"You are Veronica Renee Sellers, your mother is Della, and your father is Grant. You were born on September the sixth at nine o'clock in the evening. You like horseback riding, and you like football. You have three siblings: a brother and two younger sisters. And you have a birth mark on your left shoulder."

"Impressive! Everything I placed on the application essay. But no winner." Veronica laughed.

"Hold on! I also wrote a poem for you."

"Okay. Your last chance. It better be good. No. Never mind why don't you call me tomorrow after work. I'll listen to your poem then. Call me at five-forty-five in the afternoon."

Terry had memorized the poem he wrote about Veronica. He was ready to win her over that moment but she stopped him before hearing one word.

"Okay. I'll call you at five-forty-five," was Terry's mopey response.

"Hey, Veronica, it's me, Terry."

"Talk to you tomorrow. Bye." Veronica said with a rushed voice.

"Bye." Terry replied.

Terry would have to wait an entire day to recite this poem. He practiced all night, as he went to bed and early in the morning. He even recited the poem a couple of times during work. When five-forty-five came Terry was home and dialed Veronica's number.

She answered the phone with, "Hello."

"Hey Veronica, its me Terry."

"Hey Terry, how are you doing?"

"I'm fine."

"You know you're on my hot list, Mr. Foster."

"Yeah, I know, but I'm ready to get in your good graces."

"Well how do you expect to do that, Mr. Foster."

"I wrote a poem for you. If you like it, then I should be placed on your good list."

"Okay. It's a deal, if I don't like it you get to take me out and wash my car."

"Yes, Ms. Sellers." Terry replied with great confidence.

Well let's hear it. She requested.

Day Dream

I daydream of you every twenty-four hours
I breathe
I eat
I drink
I sleep memories of you for my sanity

I breathe to see you tomorrow and to remember yesterdays
I eat to strengthen my temple for our protection
I drink to satisfy my thirst for our existence
I sleep to dream of you in my arms

Our last touch sizzles my photographic memory
Our last kiss lingers on my lonely lips

When the time comes for me to snap out of this daydream
I pray I meet God's Heaven
Because life would be a nightmare without you!

I daydream of you every twenty-four hours
I breathe
I eat
I drink
I sleep memories of you for my sanity

I daydream of you every twenty-four hours

"Terry that's beautiful. Oh, my God, that is beautiful."

"I've been thinking about you all of this time. Did I prove it?" Terry asked with enthusiasm.

"Yeah, in so many ways you did... Tee, hold on for a second." She put the phone down and walked into the living room picked up her bible off of the coffee table.

She then rushed back to the phone. She got on her knees and delivered a quick prayer, *Thank you Lord, he's the one, I hope he is the one, please let him be the one.*

She then got up, laid on her bed and picked the phone back up and said, "Did that take too long?"

"Not at all." Terry said with a big smile.

They talked for almost two hours and towards the end of the conversation Terry told her about his present condition and how happy he was that he went to church with her.

"Do you remember the song the choir sang after Reverend Wilson finished preaching. It was *At the gate I know.*

"Yeah! Terry, I remember!" Veronica replied using a curious tone.

"Well, my Uncle Jesse used to sing that song back in my church. That day when I heard it, I thought about how lucky I was to still have my family. I hadn't witnessed a death and that I probably wouldn't know anyone at the gate."

"You're fortunate."

"Well, I said a quick prayer for my family when I thought about the song. I put my head down on the pew and prayed. As I was praying, an image of Heaven's gates came to me, then my Uncle Jesse waved goodbye to me as he walked through the gates. I was in total shock. That's when the Holy Ghost hit me."

When I got home, I called his house and he answered the phone. I was happy. We talked for an hour or so. I called him almost every other day for three weeks. The days I didn't speak to him, I prayed for his life. I told him I was just checking on things. I even said, "I love you man," before he went home this past weekend. Well, he and my dad did their usual things, but that night, they came across some bad cops." Veronica gasped. Terry continued, his voice cracking and said, "Uncle Jesse was murdered the same day he arrived home."

"Terry, I'm so sorry."

"I thought that he would have been safe at home. I didn't pray for him that day." There was a long pause while both Terry and Veronica sniffled.

"Is your dad okay?"

"Yeah, he has a bullet wound to the shoulder. But he's okay."

Veronica then said, "God knows what he's doing, just keep the faith. I know it hurts."

Veronica's voice was the only thing that made Terry feel better. They stayed on the phone for hours.

Veronica literally walked into Terry's life. As Terry took time to know her and her past, he grew fond of her. She always seemed taken aback by Terry's attitude; she didn't know whether he could be trusted or whether he was coming or going. Terry knew deep in his heart that they were supposed to get together and have an experience. He just hoped that his experience in the church would not scare her off.

Veronica's past was different than the other women that Terry had come across. She was a woman who had enough nerve to get a man into church before she even dated him. Here was a lady who said and did just enough to keep his interest. She had an independence about her that generally intimidated weak men. She was smart. She was witty and elegant in her ways. She wore respectable clothing. Some guys would think that she was high class, and she carried herself like a lady.

In the time that Terry knew her, he found out that she had had a rough experience growing up. She was an only child of a single family home. Her mom raised her after her father never showed up to the delivery room. She was terribly upset with men who did not take care of their family. Once she said, "The white man, the IRS, and even the government are not the reasons my father left my mom. It was a conscious decision to shirk his responsibilities. My father never saw my face. He just planted a seed, and he didn't care if it lived or died.

He knew I was alive. Even his family knew that I was the spitting image of their relatives. They never cared."

Terry replied, "First of all, your mom did a great job. Secondly, your dad will realize that he refused God's gift, and he will pay dearly."

Veronica then said, "I don't wish anything bad on my father, I just wish that I knew him. I hope that my children will have a full-time father.

Terry then replied, "If I'm with you, then you will not need to worry."

"Don't give me that lip service Terry. I have heard promises like that before," Veronica said with fervor.

Terry laughed and said, "Really."

Veronica had a passion for family and a good man. She had dated many guys that just were not ready for her. She had been through the same old games that every single female experiences in the dating game. She had seen almost every type of man. She said, "I have been approached by and dated the cheating man, the lying man, the quasi-invincible gangster man, the half-hearted, cowardice, brilliant educated doctor-lawyer-professional-married man. I have even seen the half-witted professional man, the not enough talent athletic man, the little man, the big man, and Lord, I have seen enough of the I-am-holy-but-capable-of backsliding-Christian man."

Terry replied, "I guess you are tired of playing games. Huh?"

"Terry, not only am I tired, I have not found a real man."

Terry then replied, "You may have with me." Veronica then laughed. "More lip service, Terry, I don't need the simple words I need action."

Veronica and Terry decided to be close friends. Terry thought of their relationship as *friends with intent.*

Chapter 15
White Women Forget

In the beginning of their quest for fairness and equality, Brenda and Terry befriended an intern, Marcha, who had just interviewed for the assistant director's position. She was a white woman from a private women's college, and she had an attitude problem. No one in the office liked her because she looked down on the support staff. She looked down on anybody who did not reflect her stances.

Dr. Prickard thought that she was a horrible team player and rejected her application. "She has no clue," he said. Terry and Brenda felt sorry for the rejected intern because they noticed that she had been used and mistreated by Prickard's gang. In spite of their misgivings, they befriended her.

There was a mandate by Prickard to get a white woman in this position. Brenda and Terry quickly found out that a woman they wanted to hire was a best friend of Prickard and his gang members. She was overqualified for the entry-level position. Brenda and Terry nicknamed her, Ms. Tweety, because she was as dizzy as a dodo bird. Terry kept saying "How come we turned down qualified people for this lady, who is clearly over-qualified? Are we doing her a favor or something?" Dr. Prickard just shook his head. Terry reminded him, "Dr. Prickard, you even said that we were looking for a young white woman to do out-of-state recruitment. And now we are about to vote on an old white woman who does not

101

want to travel. Either I'm crazy or somebody doesn't know what they want."

"Terry, I did say that, but the selection committee came with this lady."

"Well, we ought to stick to our plans and stick with what was decided. We don't need the position filled right now," Terry countered.

Prickard said, "We have done enough searching. Now, let's vote on these ladies."

Brenda and Terry voted against Tweety. Two of Prickard's gang members voted in favor of Tweety. Dr. Prickard's right-hand man, Paul Rue, decided not to make the deciding vote and waived his right to vote, which placed that decisive vote in Prickard's hand. The next day, Prickard announced that Tweety would be the next assistant director.

Six months later, in the first office meeting, Tweety was rewarded with doing things that Marcha, the intern, was in charge of. Terry stood up for Marcha and said, "I don't think Tweety should get all the recognition for the success of this project. In actuality, it was Marcha who was doing the most work."

Prickard said, "I must be honest. You're right, Terry. They both deserve credit."

Marcha came into the meeting later and gave a report on what she was doing. Terry just shook his head and laughed, saying, "Now, with all that Marcha is doing, she is literally a part-time assistant director."

Prickard said, "Yeah, I guess she is literally a part-time assistant director under (Tweety's) supervision."

Brenda responded, "It's unusual for an assistant director to supervise an assistant director. Are we preparing someone for an associate director position?"

Dr. Prickard said, "No."

Brenda replied, "Well, I want an intern with part-time assistant director responsibilities to assist me, too."

Terry said, "Me, too."

Prickard said, "We are doing just fine, and we can't afford it."

Brenda replied, "Dr. Prickard, I think we need to talk about this in private."

"No need, we'll give it considerable thought." Prickard replied effectively tabling the discussion.

Later on, Marcha said, "Thanks for setting the record straight, Terry.

You, too, Brenda."

Terry said, "It's all about being fair."

"Thanks again." Marcha finished.

There was something about Marcha that made Terry and Brenda uncomfortable. There was an attitude change that Brenda brought to Terry's attention. Marcha started talking about Dr. Prickard like he promised her the world. Dr. Prickard started showing a fondness to her that got the attention of even the gang members. One day, Terry and Brenda were talking with Marcha about the undermanned office and the terribly low salaries they were getting. Marcha stood up for Dr. Prickard as though he was a god.

One late afternoon, Terry stayed in his office until the security guard came through to lock the doors. Terry's door was closed. Marcha's desk, in the foyer where interns were generally housed, was adjacent to his office. Dr. Prickard often stopped by her desk for a few moments to carry on a conversation full of promises for Marcha. Terry overheard, "Just hang in there. You'll be rewarded in time. I promise." The two said there goodbyes and stood in the foyer a second longer than the goodbye called for. Terry listened for the smack of some lips but heard nothing. He did not see anything, but Terry felt they hugged or did something in that quick moment.

It was December, about five months after the foyer rendezvous, when Marcha showed her real colors. Out of nowhere, Dr. Prickard came into Terry's office and said, "Over the weekend, I thought about the need for a new assistant director's position. I have decided to hire Marcha as assistant director. Do you have a problem with that?"

"Do I have a choice?"

"She will be sitting in the office across from you."

"Well, we didn't hire her in the beginning because she was not personable. Now Brenda and I have to deal with her back here? She has a loud overbearing voice. I'd rather she be near you." Terry replied.

"We don't have the space, Terry!"

Terry then said, "So she is going to be an assistant director without interviewing for the position? Wow! You must have had a good weekend."

Prickard said, "Yeah, I thought about her work and decided there was no need to interview again. It was a good weekend." He overlooked Terry's scream.

Prickard left Terry's office and immediately knocked on Brenda's door. Five minutes later, Prickard left her office.

Brenda walked to her door after Prickard's departure. She walked into Terry's office, held both hands out and shrugged her shoulders. Brenda was steamed. "She didn't interview for the job. She was not the best candidate. We don't need her if Ms. Tweety would do her job. But most importantly, this girl is too conservative and racist."

"You're right, but we can't do anything. It's his world."

Marcha moved into her office. Terry greeted her with smiles and congratulations. It took Brenda and Terry a few months to get accustomed to the new co-worker. Sometimes when Brenda and Terry would get together, they would close the door to get some privacy. Once, a support person had a problem and went into Brenda's office to talk. They closed the doors. Terry was supposed to be in a meeting but returned to get his notepad. As he came around the corner, he saw Marcha eavesdropping, trying to hear what Brenda and the support person were talking about. He later told Brenda and the support person that Marcha was a traitor. Brenda just replied, "We need to pray for these people."

Terry screamed about this incident when he returned home. He wrote the following entry.

Some Folk Forget

Some folk forget the fights
Some of them forget the struggle
Some of them receive the wealth
Truly believing they did it themselves

These folk forget the bridges they crossed
Well, who built the bridge
So we all could have a voice?
Read your history, read the facts
The majority of your success
Stems from American blacks

For instance, the white women
Are the largest beneficiaries of civil rights and Affirmative actions
But the majority of them forgot
Their allies in the days of faction
Now white women are the honorary white males in Today's society

Remember when the white women had no vote,
Or the workload was too heavy for women to tote,
And the schooling for women were separate
Remember the sayings:
"No woman could be a Cadet,"
"No women will ever be President!"

Remember when sexual harassment,
Sex discrimination was the norm
And now you forget about blacks
That helped build your forum

Maybe it's part of your animal instincts
To leave your host after a symbiotic relationship
Genetics must make you use the blacks for personal gain
To get votes
To get clout and

Most importantly to place the blame
The daughters of slave owners have been improperly conditioned
But God knows who struggled to help you into your current positions
I hope you remember before your last breath
I hope you remember before God's redemption

Some folk forget the fights

Part Five

Where There is Love,

There is Life

Chapter 16
The Rich Lonely Women

Melanie was aggressive, but Terry didn't mind. He had approached so many women that it was nice to have the tables turned. They were in Jazzies, a jazz club where the thirty-thousand dollar a year millionaires drove their leased luxury cars, pretending to be rich and famous.

This was Terry's first time in this club. He had gone to Atlanta to recruit students and had to stay for three days. He was wearing a nice blazer and slacks but next to the imitation Armani, he was a bit under-dressed. Nevertheless, he felt relaxed. As soon as he found his way to the bar, he noticed a pretty chocolate brown woman with hazel eyes looking at him. He gave her the million-dollar smile and took his seat. He ordered a greyhound. The bartender said, "Oh yeah, a screwdriver." Terry smiled because he knew how to fake the millionaire role also. As he went to pull out his cash, the bartender said, "It's on Ms. Melanie."

Terry replied, "Wow! Does she look good?"

"Yeah, brother, she's the lady right there."

Terry gave her another smile and went to sit with her.

"Thanks for the drink. May I sit with you?"

"All night, Mister." She replied. Her girlfriends laughed, introduced themselves and were headed to the dance floor. At first, Terry thought she might have been the one-nighter type.

Then he decided to listen to what she had to say because she was one of the finest ladies in the club. Terry ended up buying her drinks to make things fair. They talked the entire night. She was a winner. Terry knew he would have fun with her because she was so cool. She could be his best friend, not to mention a wife. Terry thought about this before he knew her salary. She kept that part to herself. At the end of the night, they exchanged numbers and arranged to have breakfast the next day.

After the breakfast and her conversation, he was hooked. Terry hated long distance relationships, but this was one he could muster. She said the right things and acted the right way. She was a class act. Her clothing, her nails, and even her teeth were perfect. She was approaching thirty two years of age, and she was lonely, ready for marriage. They made arrangements to see each other over the next month. Terry knew she had money to spend because she went to the pay phone and stayed on it for ten minutes. Then she bought the confirmation numbers for four tickets, two departing Atlanta to Raleigh so she could visit Terry and two tickets for Terry to come to Atlanta to visit her. Terry thought to himself, *Did I just stumble on a gold mine?* She had everything at the Waffle House, tickets and itinerary. She was down to earth. She could eat at a Waffle house and afford first class seats. This was only their second meeting. This lady was unbelievable. Terry thought, *Nothing comes easy.*

Full of pride, Terry told Melanie, "I want to treat you like a superstar. I'll pay for breakfast." They hugged and Terry drove back to Raleigh. Terry felt that she was forward, but he liked that attitude. Terry told her that he would accept her friendship without a charge. He made it very clear that he didn't have a problem with her making all the money, but he had to put his two cents in every now and then. She just had to let him be the man. Terry wanted to lean on Melanie's salary. He struggled to pay rent, a car note, insurance and a stupid student loan on twenty-five thousand dollars a year. Terry dated this lady who considered herself old at thirty two. She was never married and was a super lawyer who made over one-hundred-eighty thousand dollars a year. She decided that she did not want a lawyer husband. She said, "They aren't real men."

Terry became very involved with Melanie, spending his time and living off of her perks. He still thought about Veronica, but not when he was in Atlanta. Melanie was really special. She was ready to marry anyone, and since things weren't working out between Terry and Veronica, Melanie was the perfect substitute.

They did a lot together. She liked getting away from home, vacationing with Terry. Tee knew that this couldn't last for long after she mentioned on the date that she wanted to get married. But something happened to Terry. He felt like he was falling in love with her. They dated for almost a year while Terry squeezed time in with Veronica. Terry thought that this was the lady. He was going to start talking marriage to her, but before he did, she gave him a call that he had been expecting. At least she was honest.

"Terry I'm going to the islands this weekend with some girlfriends and this lawyer friend of mine."

"Cool, baby, just enjoy yourself."

"Well, there is a little bit more to it than that."

"Go ahead." Terry said with doubt.

"This guy and I were in an on-and-off relationship. Yesterday, he asked me to marry him, and I said yes."

"Well, congratulations." Terry struggled.

"I said yes." She repeated.

"Yeah I kinda heard that the first time." Terry said with a humorous tone.

"Take care, Terry. I have enjoyed our friendship."

"Have a great one, lady, and God bless."

Terry just thought about this on-and-off relationship and was crushed. He never spoke to her again. His scream produced this entry.

On-and-Off Relations

On-and-Off relations yield spiritual turmoil and doubtful nights
Wasted love leaves a body rigid

The meek touch of flames warms your surface for survival
But still aggressive passions yearn for never-ending tranquil moments
Your search for consistency, adventurous, yet demonic
Creates a canvass of loneliness
Stained by every thought to secure stability
Within a certain amount of time

Remember that patience knows all answers
Discipline profits opportunity
And love is eternal

Never rebuke the Lamb for On-and-Off relations
Because your love waits for the eternal
Your love waits for the eternal

Chapter 17
Overseer or Over-see-her

The South has racial currents like tidal waves. Surprisingly, a white girl had the audacity to show her interest towards Tee. Terry, surprisingly, felt fear, adventure, truth and death with her every approach.

Dre and Tee had many conversations about romancing snow bunnies. They always swore that they would make sure that it would be the prettiest white woman, the one that every white man wanted, or it would be none. They laughed when ugly, fat white girls would approach friends, and their friends would go crazy. Terry's black friends would parade around with these women as if they had Ms. America when in actuality they had Ms. Poor White Trash.

Terry told Dre about Heather, who was the Miss America they talked about. She was rich, blonde, blue-eyed, caramel tanned in summer. She dressed preppy and spent her money as if there was no end. She was never known to date anyone. Terry guessed she was everyone's dream-girl in high school.

Terry often sat back and tried to think of why she liked him. Terry was articulate, smart, and a rather good-looking guy, but he could not understand why this woman would want to risk so much to get closer to him. Terry always believed that curiosity was her driving force.

Dre would always say, "I wish she wanted me!" Then he would go into graphic detail of romancing Heather. "I'd have her in this room right now!" was always his closing statements.

Terry would laugh and say, "Mama would kill you first, then the KKK would get you second, then Daddy would dig up your grave and whip you for being so stupid to sneak a white girl in this house."

Dre would then reply, "I would never let anyone know about this. I would never bring that girl to this house. Tee, I might just see what she's all about for goodness sake."

Terry was in history class with Heather, and it just so happened that she sat behind him. Terry felt her eyes on his every move, he heard his name in her giggles to friends, and he trembled with nervousness when she'd touch him to ask questions or to talk about something. Discretion was key to everything. One day, she asked him to meet her after cheerleading practice in history class. Terry's response was, "What?"

She asked him again, "Are you gonna meet me at five o'clock in this class?"

Terry said, "Okay, Sure!"

The doors to the buildings were always open after school because of various meetings and practices. Terry sneaked into the building hoping to get there before Heather. He wanted to get a feel for the environment. *Was this an ambush by the white boys or was this a joke this girl wanted to play?*

The afternoon sun gleamed through the windows of the classroom doors. The lockers were closed. The janitors had already swept the hallway. Terry tried to walk lightly because there was no telling what teachers had stayed late. He had no reason to be on the hallway. If they were caught, his alibi would be trying to find his history book. He didn't want anyone to know about this meeting, especially the black cheerleaders or any white people. The classroom doors were locked. He figured he'd have to talk to her in the hallway. As he got closer to the class, he took a deep breath and thought, *Good, I'm here first.* Terry leaned his back up against the wall beside the door and began patiently waiting on Miss America.

Within two minutes, he had checked his watch twelve times. He was nervous, and he was still ten minutes early. He leaned his head back against the wall and thought about the trouble he would get into if his parents, family or friends caught him crossing the color line. Terry figured it was easier for Heather to overcome because white guys would still consider her beautiful and acceptable regardless of what transpired. On the other hand, sisters would blackball Terry forever. Terry loved his black sisters too much to be considered a traitor. He even thought about his mom's, his aunts', and sisters' reactions and decided that he'd rather not deal with the drama.

Terry took one step towards standing Heather up. To his surprise, the classroom doorknob turned, and Heather walked out.

"You coming in or what?"

"Naw, think, I'll be going."

"Don't be afraid of me or what people will say. Please talk for a minute."

She read Terry's mind; he was impressed. Terry said, "You're right. I feel uncomfortable, but I'll talk for a little while."

Terry's sneakers squeaked into the classroom. Heather had her cheerleading practice gear on and looked beautiful with her hair pulled back.

"Terry, I have had a crush on you every since sixth grade when your mom woke you up and put you in the advanced math class."

"Really, well I'm still mad at my mama for that."

"Yeah, really, she brought you closer to me. I like her for that!" she said assertively.

Terry leaned against the blackboard and said what all eleventh graders said when surprised. "Wow!"

"I hope you know that if I could change you to a white man, I wouldn't because I like you just the way you are. If I could become black I would, but I can't. And to be honest, I like being white because it has its perks."

Terry smirked. "That's pretty cute."

Heather smiled and then said, "I have written many letters in the past month, trying to explain to you that it's okay to date if you want to. I just got tired of waiting and decided it's time to put my

115

cards on the table." She grabbed his hands. Terry's eyes focused on the connection, and the blood rushed to his head.

"Hey, I like you too. Honestly, if you were black, we'd probably hang a little, but since you're white, we have to sneak back to history class to talk. Something is wrong with this picture.

Heather became aggressive, "What do you think about this picture? She grabbed Terry's neck and pulled him to her and kissed him passionately. Terry did not stop her. He smiled and thought, *That's a good photo.*

Heather grinned as she let him go.

Terry paused and gathered his thoughts nodding his head up and down to show approval of the kiss. "Hey, I'll be honest. I have thought about you in many dreams. The thought of dating you is great, but the reality of this situation is a nightmare. For the few seconds we kissed, I was scared to death. I don't think you are ready for my reality. I live with racism everyday. I know the truth, and that's the reality of being black."

"Maybe sometime in the future we can deal with everything, but now I could only play kissing games. If I get caught, I could lose my life. All you'd have is a scarred reputation. I'm not ready for that and never will be.

Heather frowned and said, "We'll see if things can happen. I'm going to always like you."

"Cool, no problem, Heather."

They kissed again. Terry left the classroom, heading in the opposite direction of Heather. He knew that he would never take a chance like that again unless he knew it was love. Terry also did not like letting the idea of worrying about what people thought rule his life. He realized his desire for his family's and friends' respect would not allow him to cross that line.

Inspiration # 14   July 18, 1998

Overseer or (over-see-her)

The pain of the whip can still be felt
The search for freedom was a crooked hand dealt
The never-ending story of white against black
Keep keloids abundant on the black man's back

My family was broken, my ankles shackled
The blistering sun made our **dark** skin crackle
I have seen men break from your heavy hand
So you could make money from tilling Indian sands

You would hang any threat to prove a point
You placed the noose around the neck
Smacked the horse to break a joint
As I swung lifeless, some would laugh and cheer
My face filled with death, but my soul free of fear

I worked millions of hours, and you haven't given a dime
I witnessed your crimes, but you did not serve time

Oh yeah! I could hear you enter my woman's abode
She was too black to marry but good enough to hold
The white woman's bosom was just not enough
As you made skins lighter, I made your woman blush

Nowadays, your woman likes us just for show
And now they can experience the black love we know
And if I choose to over-see-her and you still consider me a foe

Overseer,
I'm just the man you love to hate
Simply because I'm **Mandingo**

Part Six

Trust is Pure and Never

Wasted, But Impurities

Spill Everyday

Chapter 18
How to Skin a Snake

In his six month stint as the assistant director of admissions, Terry knew that he was making a difference in people's lives, especially people of color. Darryl Johnson, the student from the at-risk area, enlightened Terry about his, as well as his colleagues', disposition. Terry was excited about his job. He stayed late to learn more and to get ahead. He dreamed of ways to make the job easier and more efficient. He was consumed with work and the office philosophy. When he got the job, his parents sent him a bouquet of flowers to congratulate him. His dad wrote on the card, "Terry, work for this man, as you would work for me." And Terry did.

Terry greeted the janitors early in the mornings, and security guards told him good night. His favorite cleaning person was Quintilla, an older Indian woman with a heart of gold. She would say, "Mr. Foster, what you doing here so early?" Terry would reply, "I'm here to get my students in and to see you, Ms. Quintilla." She'd laugh and say, "You see I'm here, now get them students here." Terry laughed and said, "Okay, my lady."

To say the least, Terry was very happy with his job. He thanked God regularly for allowing him the opportunity to advise young people, parents, and middle-aged students who dropped out of college. He also prayed for his director, Dr. Prickard. To Terry's dismay, Dr. Prickard was well known for being a good director with flaws. During Terry's first convention, someone came to him and said, "Well, you're the black guy in Prickard's office now."

Terry proudly said, "Yes, sir."

"Well congratulations."

"Thank you, I'm Terry Foster."

"I'm Dexter Greggs from Baylor."

"Nice to meet you."

"Same here, Terry." Dexter looked Terry over to see if he could speak his mind, to see if Terry were a real brother.

"Now does Prickard still have only two positions reserved for blacks in his office."

"Oh, yeah; things haven't changed" Terry replied, nodding his head in disgust.

"Who's the black lady in the office?"

"She's new also. Her name is Brenda Smith."

"Well, hopefully you're not the type of man Prickard wants in the office. Prickard goes after the 'Yes Masser,' token brothers that cause no problems."

"Well he chose the wrong brother." Terry said assertively.

"Terry, keep your eyes open. He's one of the best racists I've ever heard about. Don't let him change you into an institutional slave."

Terry said, "Seriously, and you haven't met him?"

Dexter continued, "I have heard enough not to want to meet him. Man, if I were you, I'd keep a journal of the things that happen in your office because Prickard will test you. He's played this game for twenty years. "

Terry sighed, "Damn! Thanks man."

Dexter said, "Don't be upset. The entire profession knows about his tactics. My director, a white woman, told me not to apply for the job because Dr. Prickard's record is undeniably racist."

Terry did not know Dexter at all, but Dexter seemed to know the facts. Dexter was right that Prickard was a politician: always politically correct, slick, and conniving with dictatorship tendencies. Prickard, the lifetime bureaucrat, had been allowed to flourish because of his university's reputation and his family name. According to his peers, he was promised the position as director by the previous director who chose "skin" favorites over a very qualified black man with more experience. Prickard was groomed for the position. He was always eloquent, nice in public and in your face, but ruthless and manipulative in his practice. Prickard knew the game better than many. Colleagues who saw Prickard rise to the top knew his mentality and knew his tactics.

Chapter 19
Uprooting His Story

Every spring, the office had a three-day staff retreat during which they reviewed the past year and prepared for the upcoming year. New employee duties were assigned, switched and critiqued. They discussed strategies and brainstormed. The retreat was held away from the office and campus to avoid interruptions and to ensure that participants were immersed in Dr. Prickard's and the university's plight during the day and dinner and pre-planned group events in the evening. Dr. Prickard decided that the Enterprise Conference Center in Lenox Falls was the ideal place to relax, contemplate, and grow together as a team.

Nothing terribly dramatic happened until the last day of the staff retreat. As Prickard went through the agenda, Terry saw major changes in employee duties that had gone unannounced the day before. Tweety-Bird's major project was quietly transferred to Marcha. There was never a mention of why this change occurred. Terry felt something was terribly wrong. Tweety then said, "Maybe Marcha should have some input in the program's design."

"Why?" Terry then asked.

Tweety answered, "That project is Marcha's baby now."

Terry was surprised that Tweety's only major project was given to Marcha. Tweety now had fewer duties and had been getting paid more than any assistance director. Terry then reviewed the former employee's responsibilities list from the previous year. With a few exceptions, Tweety's workload looked identical to the former employee's workload.

These comparisons showed that Dr. Prickard had lied and was paving the way for Tweety to be the next associate director. With the change, she had supervisory experience where Marcha didn't.

Dr. Prickard seemed uncomfortable when Terry challenged the change.

Terry remembered that Penny had been labeled an Assistant Director, but, to his knowledge, was still being paid the same amount. Terry was wondering what salary change Prickard would make for Penny given that Penny was not from their high society loop. Penny finally received an appropriate title after doing the same thing for three years. Prickard did not give Penny a raise with her title, because Penny was not of their social group.

The retreat was the perfect setting for asking questions. Dr. Prickard could not use his eloquent, evasive answers. He would have to answer these questions truthfully or lie to the entire staff. Terry knew he could be fired on the spot, but it was a risk he was willing to take. Terry's opportunity to ask several direct questions came during the General Office Concerns section of the agenda.

"Where do you see the office in the next couple of years?"

Dr. Prickard answered the question with projections of new things to satisfy demands for customer service.

"What will the office make-up be, since you have this new position the Vice Provost of Enrollment Management and Director of Admissions and you may be leaving soon?"

As he answered, he mentioned Paul Rue as a prospect for his position and the necessity of a national search. Prickard also could foresee an associate director's position becoming available along with requesting two new assistant director positions.

Terry then asked if he saw any significant increase potential in salaries of the office, especially for those people who might want to stay longer.

Dr. Prickard replied, "According to national trends, our salaries are higher than our peers. More than likely, they will remain the same. Of course, that's contingent on the state allocations for our budget and receipts from application fees and merit raises.

Brenda addressed the competitiveness of the salaries. "Something seems wrong when other institutions have larger professional staffs and are able to pay their employees competitively. We're the largest university in the system, and we handle more students than they do."

Dr. Prickard explained, "Our system of pay is different than that of other institutions, but we're competitive." He failed to mention that he was one of the highest paid people in the system, getting a cozy one-hundred-and-four-thousand dollars per year. The next person in command earned forty-thousand a year.

Terry could tell that Dr. Prickard was agitated by these questions. Terry leaned back and placed both hands behind the head. Then Dr. Prickard reverted to an offensive tactic. To unnerve Terry, Prickard got very personal and told the professional staff that Terry had been looking for a job with the University of Virginia at Arlington. He said, "I'm sure Terry will find that salaries at this institution are similar and competitive. Large salaries are not a part of the package for assistant directors of admissions."

Terry looked at Brenda and then the rest of the staff and smiled. Terry knew that the information he knew about office history would be the perfect reply at this time. Tee was not shocked by Prickard's attack. In fact, the attack really opened the doors for the burning questions Terry wanted to ask many times throughout the year.

Then Prickard said, "I will be frank with you, Terry, and anyone else. If you don't feel that you are getting what you deserve here, I suggest you look for another job."

Now, Terry was shocked that he had brought everyone else into the conversation. Everyone looked at him and thought, *I can't believe he said that.* Some of Prickard's gang changed posture; others shook their heads in utter disbelief. Dr. Prickard's red face showed that he was embarrassed about the last comment. He had shown his true feelings. He didn't care about his staff, even the employees close to him.

Terry said, "In other words, you don't care how we live our lives outside of this office. If we can't pay bills, or buy food, or clothing, you don't care. Just as long as we come in and do our work and cause little commotion, you don't care."

Everyone's eyes turned back to Prickard. They all wondered, 'Is he right,' Dr. Prickard?

Prickard used Paul Rue as an example. He said, "If Paul were to leave, and please don't leave, Paul, then we would have to hire someone who could replace him—not at his current salary, but at a competitive starting salary because people with computer backgrounds are in high demand."

Dr. Prickard continued, "Assistant director's positions, although real good jobs, do not dictate higher starting salaries."

Terry had had enough. "Richard." Terry shocked everyone by calling him by his first name. "How do you decide on everyone's raises, what is the driving force behind these raises, and are starting salaries project-driven?"

Terry continued without taking a breath, "We all worked very hard last year, and I'm quite sure we are all looking for some good raises. I really enjoy what I am doing and I just need to know how the future will look for assistant directors who stay to work here."

Dr. Prickard answered saying, "Salaries will always be competitive, but it would be difficult to assess individual projects to determine raises."

Terry asked, "Well, Richard, how do you justify starting salaries being non-negotiable for some and negotiable for others when we all do the same job? I know there has been tremendous disparity in the ranges of the salaries in this office, including yours.

Dr. Prickard then said. "How can you say there is a big difference in starting salaries, Terry? Everyone is judged according to what they bring to the office."

Terry apologized before he spoke, "I'm sorry, everyone, but I have to bring this to the floor." He continued, saying, "It was my understanding that every assistant director started out at twenty-five-thousand dollars per year and that the salary was non-negotiable. But now we have people who started after me and Brenda who are being paid more. Some are being paid less." Terry stated the starting salaries of the assistant directors in the room. "Tweety started at twenty-seven-thousand, but Penny and Marcha started at twenty-two thousand."

Then Terry asked, "And, Richard, how can you justify giving Christina Collins an eight-and-half percent raise when in fact she started out making more money? I presume she had a master's degree with a little experience, but what did she do to warrant such a big raise?"

Dr. Prickard explained that Christina Collin's raise was based on that year's budget, a budget that determined everyone except the African-American assistant directors would receive a tremendous raise. Dr. Prickard was truly taken aback by Terry's direct questions and fumbled through justifying his previous actions.

Terry said, "Richard, this is what's happening, and I have a great concern for my welfare. Everyone else should be concerned also. When you start people off at low salaries, no matter how well they do, they cannot ever close the gap between their counterparts who start off with higher salaries. Their percentage raises would have to double or triple in order to be equal. I only want you to consider changes in this area because I feel as though the office has a design that makes African-Americans go search for other positions more frequently."

At that point, Dr. Prickard moved around in his chair and agreed with Terry. Lisa Mc Donald, a staunch supporter of Prickard, even noted that there was high turnover among the non-professional staff also.

Dr. Prickard sarcastically said, "No good deed goes unpunished."

"What does that mean?"

Dr. Prickard said, "With respect to Christina Collins' salary increase, no good deed goes unpunished."

Terry turned and said, "In all fairness, everyone deserves that type of raise. We bust our butts for this office. But I would not consider it a good *"deed"* if it satisfies one and hurts others. I consider that favoritism."

The retreat ended, and Terry got into the BMW he had borrowed and drove off with a feeling of relief. The ball was in Prickard's court. How would he respond to his tactics being exposed?

When Terry turned onto Interstate 40 to go back home, he saw a tree that had been burned. He thought about his friends back home, his dad and Uncle Jesse. He laughed and said, "One day, one of my people will uproot that old Hangman tree." He paused then said, "I have just knocked down that old limb, Uncle Jesse, and it felt good."

Terry thought about a gang mentality analogy. Prickard was the leader, and Paul Rue was the right-hand man. The ladies were spineless followers of the leader. Mrs. McDonald had been there many years before Terry and Brenda and had seen people come and go. The black duos before Terry had experienced the same thing: a beating from Prickard and the gang members. They did not want outsiders in the gang, especially blacks.

They were an elitist gang, giving out orders, taking the largest salaries, and issuing threats of unemployment. They didn't even want white people without the proper background. There was a veteran white woman who had been there for thirty years that could have run the entire office. But she was not a part of the elite. After thirty years, she was making a dismal thirty-thousand-dollars a year. A young white, blonde woman or Paul Rue, the brown nose king of the office, would surpass that amount within a year.

Terry had had enough. He wrote the letter that Dr. Prickard requested as an evaluation of Prickard's performance. Prickard never thought that an employee would tell him the truth. Terry found this letter it easy to write. He wrote:

Dr. Prickard,

My opinion of your leadership has changed in many ways. Last year, I mentioned that you are fair to all employees. It is amazing how inaccurate this statement has become. Now, I see a leader who only cares about being politically correct, and not just correct.

I took the liberty of finding out information about salaries and raises. As you know, I was not pleased. You have an unusual and unethical favoritism towards certain professional staff members. I also question your hiring of professional staff members. One is overqualified, and the other is very difficult to work with. Under the normal democratic interviewing process, these people would not have been voted into the positions. I have to assume that you manipulate rules and regulations to satisfy a personal agenda.

I will never forget when I needed a raise to overcome expenses associated with my car and living arrangements. You told me that raises are given after the budget has been settled, sometime in July. I later found out that you gave a co-worker a raise in the same month! When I brought these discoveries and other concerns to your attention, you responded, "Maybe you should find another job."

My first year, I was overwhelmed with the politically correct leadership qualities I thought you possessed. However, I am truly disappointed in your internal beliefs. Your flawless demeanor belies a lack of concern for certain employees.

It's been approximately three months since we have come to this professional disagreement. I have and will continue to work with you, even though these problems will not be corrected. Orison Sweet Marine's quote exemplifies my personal perspective to this job. He says, *"The greatest thing a man can do in this world is to make the most out of the stuff that has been given him. This is success, and there is no other."* I will continue to be successful and a diligent worker regardless of what obstacle is in my path.

> Terry R. Foster
> Assistant Director of Admissions

Prickard read the letter in astonishment. Prickard approached Terry the next day to do what was politically correct. They talked about his problems and then Prickard said, "I'll take your comments into account."

Terry thought, *Yeah, right!*

Chapter 20
Divorce: A Mistake or a Blessing?

Brad knocked on Terry's door at about four o'clock. Terry opened the door and said, "What's up, man?"

Brad didn't answer. He came in, sat down, and placed the unopened fifth of Jack Daniels on the kitchen table.

"Baby, I want a divorce." Brad mumbled to Terry. Then Brad gave the matter serious thought.

"That's all this heifer had to say after three years of marriage and five years of dating." Brad opened the bottle and took a big swallow.

Terry stood speechless. Brad then mumbled, "All she said was 'Baby, I need a divorce.' And all I did was look." Brad wore the faceless expression he had worn with Shelia.

Terry remained silent. He couldn't think of anything intelligible to say.

"Terry, I felt like breaking her neck. I thank the Lord I didn't, but I felt like it." Brad took another big gulp.

"We don't need to go there, partner! Maybe she'll change her mind," Terry interjected in a hushed mumble. Then Terry said, "Let me get some of that liquor, man." Terry went to his kitchen cabinet, pulled two glasses, turned to the refrigerator, and pulled out the ice tray. He sat beside Brad at the kitchen table and poured two drinks.

"Hey man, I don't think that Shelia will change her mind. She packed her bags and moved to her sister's house in Atlanta."

Brad put his hands near his temples, wiping what appeared to be sweat and tears from his face. Then he quickly jumped up and headed for the door.

Terry immediately said, "Give it some time. Don't go there raising hell. Plus, I don't have the cash to get you out of jail. You put a good dent in this fifth of Jack Daniels, and DUI is a mother."

Brad shook his head and came back to the table for another drink. Terry got the quilt and pillow and tossed it to Brad for the couch. Brad laughed saying, "Yeah! I guess you're right!"

They talked all night long about women, marriage, divorce, and the importance of friends.

Brad had always been top-shelf when it came to friends. Terry and Brad had been hanging for years, throughout high school and college. Brad was an intellect, but rugged in style of dress and appearance. His upbringing put emphasis on hard work, not the fetishes of designer clothing and personal appearance. Gucci watches and Donna Karan were important to city kids like his wife, Shelia. Brad and his friends were strictly ball players with a wardrobe from sports athletic stores. It was not until the twelfth grade that they decided to become selective about clothing and appearance. Brad could be comfortable both ways, white collar or blue collar, but he would choose baggy jeans, boots, and a triple XL Karl Kani shirt and a cap every time, if possible.

Strangers and even so-called friends feared Brad. His intense facial structure, six foot four inch, two-hundred-and-twenty-pound chiseled frame, and an unmanageable temper made many people assume trouble. However, Brad had more sense than many people expected. A double major in engineering and physics and a keen knowledge of computers made Brad very marketable. Brad and friends were always drinking and partying around the nearby neighborhoods and playing ball, cards or with girls. Brad never cared about anyone other than Shelia. He dated many women, but she was the first love.

After Brad's college graduation, he got a great job with a major pharmaceutical company. Everything was going right for Brad in the professional world. He was making sound money, and in two years, Brad was able to get debt-free and take control of his future.

Shelia had moved to Brad's high school district to avoid the problems with city schools. Shelia was also an intellect. She graduated from highschool with honors and went on to college where she majored in business management and graduated at the top of her class. She was not the rugged type but spent time around the athletes. Shelia had a down-to-earth attitude and heartwarming kindness. She was beautiful and independent, open and respectful. She and Brad were perfect for each other. The majority of their friends dubbed them as most likely to celebrate seventy years of marriage. Their opposites complemented each other perfectly.

Shelia was Brad's dream girl, and she could do no wrong. Brad would stand up to the outrageous but would become easily humbled in certain situations, and that worried Terry.

Shelia loved Brad for being a responsible, down-to-earth young man, with great potential. Brad loved her as a best friend and soul mate. This type of love was unbalanced, and that had worried Terry, too.

As the discussion moved into the night, Terry thought about marriage in a different light. Terry, a single man, proud to have his freedom, and never lonely, by some weird twist of faith, became the marriage counselor for Brad, who was lonely and didn't want freedom. Many times during talks with Brad, Terry thought, *Is marriage worth it?*

It would be a couple of months after the Jack Daniels visit that Terry would hear from Brad. Terry screamed over Brad's situation and created this entry for his journal.

One-Hundred-Eighty-Degrees
From Paradise

Any way I turn, I'll be in paradise
Either you're with me, or it's just me
Roller coasters break tough men
But not real couples

Touch the burner; I've learned that lesson
Watch that step; I've fallen before
Break the law; I'll serve my time
Wear a jacket, or catch the flu
I'll be in paradise no matter what you do!

Sympathy mixed into decisions is a crying shame
Tell me the truth and respect my gains
No time for pity
No will for lies
Look me in the eyes
Say what's on your mind
I'll be in paradise regardless of what you decide

Our dreams are unparalleled
And the Universe may darken
As glitter needs light
There will be no bargains

I exist to succeed with you by my side
I exist without you with God on my mind
There is one answer and no need to say please
Because my trip to paradise is
One- hundred-and-eighty-degrees

Chapter 21
Queva? Married?

Sometimes women approach ex-boyfriends, ex-associates or ex-husbands to test the boundaries of new relationships. Queva met Jason, and six months later, they were engaged. It was immediately after Terry decided to leave Queva alone and walk away from the relationship. Queva had recognized Terry as one of her best friends. She still would have liked calling him and talking about their past. After ten months without a word, her voice was refreshing to Terry. Terry said, "You know I still love you, but we are crazy together."

Queva would reply, "I'm crazy over you! "

"Yeah, me, too!"

After small talk, Queva admitted the purpose of the call. "Terry, I need to tell you that I am engaged. Jason and I are getting married!"

"Congratulations," he said in a despondent voice. "I heard from someone a couple of weeks ago. I'm over the surprise. Thanks for telling me, though."

"I tried getting in contact with you for months. I even called your mother and sister."

Terry feigned a distraction. "Hold on for a second. I have a student in the office." Actually, Terry had to take a break. The words coming from her mouth made his stomach hurt. Terry had thought that after a year or two and regular contact with each other, they would try it again. Then he would marry Queva. Terry never figured that he would lose Queva to Jason.

When he returned, Terry fired off a round of questions, "Who is this Jason? Are you sure you're in love? Are you pregnant? You need to be patient with marriage."

Queva said, "Things haven't changed. My dad's still in his skin, and he is not Terry Foster."

Terry calmed down and said, "Commercial break! Let's change the channel.

"I'm happy for you baby. I'm just jealous of any relationship that involves you and marriage. I always believed that you were mine forever. I was wrong."

Queva said, "Thanks Terry, it makes me feel good that you can accept my being married. Plenty has happened since we've been apart. I only hope that you can feel the happiness I feel. I still care for you immensely."

Terry then said, "What if I told you I need to see you?"

"I don't know. I think we need to bring some closure to our relationship. Here and now." She replied.

Terry said, "Not the choice I want you taking but smart choice. I don't know if I'll ever see you again, but take care and goodbye."

She said, "Can I call you back?"

Terry said, "No need to ask. It'll be good to hear from you."

They talked each day for the next three days. When it was over, Terry lay on his bed with a empty heart and an active mind. Terry couldn't stand it any longer; he had to get this problem solved. Terry had to scream this situation to see what his soul was saying about the feelings he had for Queva. His soul came up with this passage.

Caught in the Middle

I've been thinking of you daily, and this feeling I can't control
You were my reason for smiling; you have been my life's goal
I can still see your picture, I can still feel you touch
I can remember only good things, and it hurts so much

It's been years since I have touched you
It's been years since we kissed
The Lord knows I still love you; he won't let me forget
Will you ever let my heart beat the way it did before?
I'm in need of your love and
I can't take this pain any more

I'm caught in the middle of a war with myself
When will I let go of memories and learn to love someone else?
I'm caught in the middle of pain and sinful deeds
The thought of you being married still doesn't stop my needs

I'm caught in the middle of true love and destiny
Please make my wish come true; bring reality
And I'm caught in the middle of choosing the protocol
Should I walk up to you, or just give a call

I know you still think about us, and I know you still care
You rushed into a wedding hoping I would stop you there
Yes, you'd meet me anywhere?
You have no fear?
Well no, I don't think that's a good idea
We shouldn't meet here!
I think I just miss you, and I needed to know you care

I'm caught in the middle of a war with myself
When will I let go of memories and learn to love someone else?

Chapter 22
Brad Chooses the Blessing

Brad chose to put all of his faith in the Lord. He decided that there was nothing that he could change. Shelia's heart had been hardened. She was a total disappointment to Brad and his family. Brad hated the thought of dating another woman when he knew that his wife was supposedly the only person for him. The divorce papers came quickly. Brad hesitated in signing them, but he soon found strength and humility to let her fly away.

He knew that one day the pain he was experiencing would go away. Brad knew that he had not given up on Shelia. She gave up on him. Brad knew that one day this woman would realize that she left the best man for her. As the ink dried, Brad realized that he was alone. The only people that would be by his side were his true friends and family. He struggled through depression and drinking and even went on a dating spree to forget about Shelia.

No one compared. Brad decided that he had cried his last tear. Now was the time to get back on cloud nine. He decided to put his time in two things: his work and his church. He decided that he would make a living in these two areas. Brad tithed and worked to tithe.

Before Shelia had been gone one year, Brad received two promotions. Brad had decided to work diligently to become independent, and to his rewards, he started his own business. It had been eighteen months since Shelia left. Brad had deposited nine thousand dollars in his savings account. With this new attitude, he had a salary well over ninety-thousand-dollars a year. With great pride, he tithed ten percent of his salary into the church.

Brad stayed in contact with Terry during his transformation. Brad thanked Terry for his friendship, but the one thing that made Terry feel great was that Brad said, "Tee, I was always one-hundred-eighty degrees from paradise. Thanks for the poem. It helped me to get on the right track."

Terry then asked, "Do you think you'll get married again?"

Brad smiled and said, "In the beginning I would have said, 'Hell no.' But now with understanding life's struggles, I would take a woman that was compatible with me. Not an average woman."

Terry couldn't wait to get home and scream about Brad's answer. He screamed for a few minutes about the average woman. Terry was pleased with the entries.

Average Woman,
My Love is Not For You?

My love is not made for the average woman
My love is made for you
You create an energy that surpasses the sun's heat
But yet my love cools your body to a refreshing warmth

The mental comprehension of our love
Confuses those who try to mock our relationship
We are the perfect balance as long as Jesus is our Savior
I could love beyond immortal reins
I could touch your heart with Words, never pain
My heart beats because you breathe
My faith is stronger because you believe

Sweetheart, if I can truly be yours
The sunlight, the moon and the waters will always assure
That I am the only one for you
Substitute or replacements are strictly taboo

My love is not made for the average woman
My love is made for you
I will love beyond the stars
And I will love through relationship wars

He will make Heaven a home
For we reap what we sow
And Christ fed us, not our foes
Therefore, my love will never die
My love is not for the average woman
My love is only for you

The Love Pond

Satisfied in a subtle way
Learning more and more
Hoping compatible experiences arise
The conversation flows, our pond is never dry
A catch for anyone
Not a catch for me

Many swim in the sea
But one exists for my pond
Just because your attention is caught
Does not mean that you swim on this farm

The water is fresh, no salt in this body
No dip for immediate pleasure
Until His Son controls the weather
Live by his measures,
Then our love is a pond for the Heavens

Then a good catch for anyone
A great catch for me

Until His Son controls your weather
You're just another swim in the sea.
I prefer a pond for two
Because His love watches over me

The greatest catch for you
But you must understand
The Love pond is made for Him
The greatest catch for me

Part Seven

It's God's Fight, and

I'm His Soldier

Chapter 23
Grandma's Quilt

Grandma was always sitting on her screened front porch, wearing her flowery housecoat and slippers. She'd spend hours talking to friends who visited or people who called to see how she was doing. When Terry and his family came home for the fourth of July, everyone convened at Grandma's house. Normally, everyone would spend time making her feel like the Queen of England. They came with work clothes on and tools in hand. The men would work outside, and the women would work inside.

Grandma had a old shed that Terry, Dre, and Cousin Andrew were in charge of cleaning. This year, the entire immediate family with the exception of Uncle Jesse and Granddad who had both passed, were home for the occasion. She was happy to see all her grandchildren and sons and daughters. She was pleased to see everyone making her lawn and home immaculate. Grandma had her sons grilling and cutting firewood and cutting grass. When they went into the house for drinks of water, the ladies had the entire house smelling like fresh lemon and chlorine. They were cooking, cleaning, wiping, mopping, or rearranging furniture to Grandma's specifications. The entire family took time to let Grandma know how they felt. Grandma would say, "It's the small things people do that count more with me. You don't have to buy presents or give me money; just spend time with me. But since y'all insist on cleaning, keep right ahead. Keep right ahead. I've cleaned up after all y'all children, and you owe me a little."

Terry was cleaning the top floor of the shed and found an old wooden box filled with memorabilia from when his grandparents were growing up. There was a photo album with old tattered and torn black-and-whites. There was clothing that Granddad used to wear, a shiny gold watch, and his pocket knife. At the bottom of the box lay a beautiful, handmade quilt. It was unmarked, undamaged. The quilt was about seven-foot wide and six-foot long and at least an inch thick. One side of the quilt was the traditional patch work of polka dots and stripe patches in every color imaginable. On the other side, the background color was sky blue with clouds and the sun in the right corner. A red barn and old house were to the far-left corner of the quilt. In a distant background beside the house, there were black kids playing a kick ball game. Superimposed in the center of the quilt was a bright gold and yellow haystack that took up the majority of the quilt.

Dre asked, "Tee, where did you get that from?"

"This old cedar box."

"That's nice; you need to show Grandma what you found."

"Yeah, I'm going to do that right now."

Terry walked up to the house with the massive quilt. When he got to the house, he walked by a group of aunts. Aunt Tricia said "Oh, that's Mama's quilt." Every aunt and female cousin came to see the quilt. Grandma, who had come out of her bedroom, came to see what the commotion was about. She asked, "What old picture did y'all find this time?"

Aunt Tricia said, "Mama, look at what Tee found in the shed."

Grandma placed both hands over her mouth and gasped, "It's mama's quilt." She starting crying. Aunt Tricia grabbed grandma by the waist and pulled the old woman to her side. The quilt laid over the couch.Grandma and everyone else, except Terry, had a tear in their eyes. Grandma looked at Terry and said, "It's your great grandma's quilt, Terry. She made this before I was born, and it covered the bed in the cold winters for company. Mama made it before 1897 and kept it in her cedar trunk. I was born in 1911 and started practicing sewing on the patchwork on the back. She pointed to Aunt Mary and said, "Turn to the back side," Mary.

"When I was nine years old, I started on this scarlet patch and did the entire backside. I bet you're wondering why it's so heavy. That because there is about four generations of patchwork on this quilt. Mama told me if someone were to cut through this blanket, they'd be cutting up one-hundred-year-old fabric. I did the repair; Tricia did some patch work on the back. She started right here. You remember, Tricia?

"No ma'am!"

"You were too young to remember when I first taught you how to sew."

"I added the sun to the front. I think my mama sewed the children playing. It has been twenty years since I have seen this blanket, and it looks just like new. That's my grandma's old house right there."

Grandma started crying again. Terry's mom hugged grandma and shed a tear.

Terry couldn't wait to get back to his apartment to scream about this quilt. He felt there was some unfinished business about the quilt, beautiful as it was. He knew that if he screamed, he could find out what his great-great grandma and these ladies were trying to say.

Terry did his regular routine and started screaming. He prayed for God to guide him. He laid his head back with pen and paper in hand. Exactly one hour later, his note pad was filled with a very unique passage. Terry felt the presence of spirits and souls. Following the passage, there were about forty names. He guessed they were friends of the family. Three of the names were of rich black people from his grandma's neighborhood, but he didn't recognize the others. The other names were unknown. Then Terry read what he had written. He was amazed. He felt as though he had come up with what his great-grandmother was trying to tell him. The following weekend, he got his journal and a change of clothing, and he and his Nissan pick-up headed to South Carolina. He was anxious to talk with his grandma about the quilt, the poem and the lists of names. He prayed to God, *Please let her be in the best of health when I get there.*

149

Four hours later, Terry pulled into the Grandma's front yard. Grandma was on the porch, just as Terry figured. Terry got out of the truck with journal and travel bag in hand. He could hear his Grandma talking to Aunt Tricia, who was sitting beside her. "Tricia, Tee is here!"

"Yeah, Ma! That's Tee!" Aunt Tricia happily replied.

Terry said with a jovial voice, "Hey pretty ladies, how y'all doing?"

"We doing fine, Tee! Come on in, and give Grandma a hug."

Aunt Tricia unlocked and opened the screen door. Then she hugged and kissed her nephew. Terry walked to the rocking chair where Grandma sat and hugged and kissed her. Terry asked "What y'all doing?"

"Me and your grandmother are resting. We been working all day, Tee."

"Yeah baby, Tricia and I been working on that ol' quilt you found. We talked about you earlier today."

"Oh yeah, that's why my ears have been ringing. Y'all been talking 'bout me, huh?"

"We sure were." Aunt Tricia said.

"What if you hadn't been cleaning up that old shed down there? We never would have found that quilt. Tricia said that you always had a different attitude than the other kids.

"I told Tricia that you'd be coming back to see me. And guess what? Here is where you are, boy."

Tee said, "Yeah, you knew I was coming, huh?"

"Mama said you'd be coming back yesterday about this time."

Terry laughed and said, "You sure are right; I'm here."

Terry walked from the porch into the kitchen and said, "What have you got to eat, Grandma?"

She said, "There's plenty in there, boy. Get something."

As Terry brought his plate out of the kitchen, he saw the quilt lying on the dinner table, patchwork side up. He smiled.

Terry took his plate back to the front porch and began eating. He said, "Grandma, I've got something I want to show you." He opened his bag, pulled out his journal and turned to his entry. His grandmother read his list and poem and shook her head in disbelief. She looked at Terry and said, "You are very special, Terry."

Terry said enthusiastically, "You like it?"

"I love it, Terry. You are very special, baby. We got to talk."

"Okay, Grandma, we'll talk, but let me get another biscuit, Okay?"

"Go ahead, son."

As he entered the kitchen this time, Grandma started crying with joy. Terry noticed Aunt Tricia had turned the quilt on the picturesque side. He noticed the changes and additions Tricia and Grandma made to the quilt. It was unbelievable. Within in a second, Terry fell to the floor, breaking his plate and dropping his biscuits.

Grandma hollered, "Is everything alright in there?!"

Tricia ran to the screen door, "Mama, Tee fainted!

They ran to his rescue with water and a pillow for his head. Tee came out of his shock a minute or two later. He was shaking with chills.

"How you feeling, baby? You just fainted, that's all. Lean up and let me put the ice pack on the back of your neck." Grandma helped him to sit up. They were facing the blanket portion that hung off the edge of the table.

Terry said, "Grandma, why did you sew the needles on the quilt?"

Grandma said, "Baby, don't worry. You got the gift. Everything will be okay."

"What gift?"

"You have the gift that my mama had. You can hear souls. That's how you know what to write and how people feel. Mama told me a grandchild would probably have the gift. She used to tell me about her experiences with deep thought and meditation. She thought she was crazy, and she never told Papa, but she told me

151

because I knew she wasn't crazy. I knew you were the special one, but I didn't think you had the gift until you found this quilt.

"Honey, your Grandma and Aunt Tricia had stitched in names of folk beside the needles they stitched. The needles had a shine or sparkle that took the shape of the holy cross. The names you thought about were the names of rich white folk and rich black folk who have helped this family many years ago. These people are angels, and when judgement day comes, one of our children will give this quilt to the Lord.

Terry couldn't believe what had happened. He sat across from the quilt and started reciting the poem he had written about the quilt.

Are You the Needle?

Are you the needle in the haystack?
Do you shine like no other?
Or are you tarnished and
Undercover?

Are you the white boy
Who gives the birdie
Hiding safe behind a windshield
You thought was sturdy?

Are you the white girl
That points the finger
Trying to save face
Hoping rumors won't linger?

Are you the policeman that lied on the stand?
Are you a judge with unbalanced hands?
Are you the juror that ignored the evidence?
Are you the attorney that manipulated words and their contents?

Are you the banker with the corrupt loans?
Are you the city councilmen dumping in racial zones?
Are you the salesclerk that follows me through the stores?
Are you the employer who discriminates behind closed doors?

Are you quick to assume I am a gun toting goon?
Or are you the teacher that placed a future scholar
In a curriculum for buffoons?
Are you the needle in the haystack?
Do you see the Red, the Yellow, the White and yeah, the Black?
Did you drop from Heaven
Ready to work in days of seven?
Will I find you in the midnight glow
Like the Underground Railroad's back door?

I have come across much hay
That should be fodder for the animals
And ready for decay
If this barn were to burn on Judgment Day
Would you rather be needles
Or just the plain hay?

I hope you are the one
That we've been looking for
Ready to mend the wounds
Sew the cuts and cure the sores
Will you go through Judgment's door?
Are you the needle we've been looking for?
Are you the needle we've been looking for?

Chapter 24
Gang Mentality

It was July 28, 1997, when Terry made one of his most interesting entries into his journal. The entry was inspired by the actions of Dr. Prickard and the campus police. After talking with Dexter Greggs, the informant, Terry began his own research to see if Dexter's claims were right. Terry went to the library and the employee's concerns office to find out the history of this admissions office under Dr. Prickard and other directors. He found more than he expected. He shared his findings with Brenda, a few others that had been mistreated, and even the ones who were treated like saints. Some people were tremendously upset with the discrepancies with respect to color and sex.

Prickard had set up the appointments to discuss raises. Terry was anxious to see what type of raise he was going to receive, as he and Brenda were not eligible until the end of one year's employment. Terry knew that he had done one of the best jobs among the entry-level people. His training curve was less than a month. He had started taking appointments and public speaking within two months, and people thought that Terry had always been there. Terry had great teamwork skills and an individual drive that would have made any manager desire him as an employee.

Within six months, Terry had taken on new duties due to Christine Collins leaving her position. Terry was fully trained to read and advise international students, as well as his regular duties. He never forgot the statement that Christine Collins made when she was training him for international student advising: "Terry, this job will pay off. Dr. Prickard gave me a very good raise because I accepted the international students. I'm quite sure he'll reward you in the same manner." Her statement gave Terry hope.

Terry took a seat in Prickard's office. They discussed his first year in review. Prickard praised Terry for everything. "Terry, I have been utterly pleased with your work ethic, professionalism, personality, and teamwork skills. Everyone in this office appreciates your hard work. You are very valuable to this team."

"Thanks, Dr. Prickard. I love this job."

Prickard rambled on for a few minutes, explaining the budget. Then he said, "Well, Terry you're getting one of the biggest raises this office has seen." Terry's eyes blinked with anticipation." You're getting a four-and-a-half percent raise. You should be very proud."

Terry was shocked, dumbfounded, and insulted. Terry knew that the blonde with the similar duties, same background, and similar work habits had gotten a eight-and-a-half percent raise. The only thing Terry said was "Thanks." The next hour, he sat behind his closed office door. He knew he had to talk to Dr. Prickard to get a better raise. Terry buzzed Prickard on the phone and arranged for a fifteen minute appointment to discuss some concerns.

"Dr. Prickard, I don't think a four-and-a-half percent raise is a good raise."

"Why do you say that?"

"Well, I am doing international students in addition to my regular duties—a heck of a lot more than what Christine was doing before she left. You gave her an eight-and-a-half percent raise after her first year, not to mention you gave her a thousand-dollar signing bonus on her salary when you hired her. I was expecting the same."

Prickard turned red in the face. He knew that Terry had the audacity to research his actions. His faced turned even brighter as Terry concluded, "Now exactly what is she doing to deserve this type of raise when the state only gives a two percent raise? Exactly what does a candidate have to do to be treated fairly?"

Prickard's face told the story. He then said, "Terry, last year's budget was different, and there were some factors that I'd rather not discuss."

Terry replied, "There must be some substantial factors. That's a big raise. I haven't seen one black get a raise close to that number."

Dr. Prickard said, "Different circumstances, different people, a different time. Don't worry about it. I treat everyone fairly."

"So after all those compliments and urging me to keep up the good work, you don't feel that this is the time to reconsider this raise?"

"I can't, Terry. The paperwork has already been sent to the payroll office."

"I'm quite sure if you were paying too much, you could change it."

Prickard did not answer.

"Well, that's going to put me in a position where I have to find a better paying job."

Prickard stared at Terry. He then looked down at some paperwork on his desk, picked up a file, and began reading.

"I believe you only care about white lives in this office. You have a problem, and your history shows it, Richard." Terry walked out of his office and looked back at the man he used to call Dr. Prickard.

Prickard was shocked to hear his first name. Prickard had a look on his face that would forever remain in Terry's mind. Prickard knew that Terry figured out that he was a racist. He knew that the man behind the mask had been revealed. Prickard knew that he had a real black man in the office, one who would not allow him to passively succeed in his racist agenda. Prickard thought, *This is a real nigger.*

At about six-forty-five that evening, the campus police came into the building, checking to make sure the office doors were closed and locked. Fred was a black man who worked on the force for twenty years. He stopped by Terry's office because the light was still on and the door was open. To Fred's surprise, Terry still was sitting in his chair, deep in thought about what had transpired between him and Prickard.

Fred said, "Working late, partner?"

"No, just thinking about some of the racist people in this office."

"Oh, yeah. You had a run in with Prickard, huh?"

"Yeah, a good one."

"Don't worry. They are all over this campus."

"Well, let me tell you about this cracker. Forgive me, Lord."

Terry went on to explain what had happened. At the story's end, Fred said, "I have been on this force for twenty years. These honkies have looked over me for a promotion every year I was eligible. They have to pay me well because of time served, but they don't want me to have the authority. I know more about this police office than every white boy they bring in to be commander. They have to ask me so much, I get tired of them.

"In the beginning, I was goal oriented. I wanted to be qualified for that position as soon as possible. By my fourth year, I should have had at least one promotion. I had come in blind, thinking that I'd be treated fairly, but the only thing I did was spin my wheels in their bull-crap. I have more experience than anyone they've hired in the past twelve years. I don't want the headache now—I'd refuse it the second they offered it to me. But guess what, they will never offer it."

Fred came into the office and sat down. "In my sixth year here, I realized that those crackers don't care about us. I remember when these white boys from fraternity row snatched a twelve-year-old black boy who was riding his bike. They dragged him about thirty yards into the nearby woods and castrated him. A jogger could hear him crying. He was rushed to the hospital and survived. The boy had a good description of his attackers. To my commander's disbelief, the clues went straight to a fraternity house. Those boys never admitted anything, and we never searched for evidence. Those boys got off Scott-free. The crackers claimed they couldn't find the culprits. The news didn't report it. Those cracker's just don't care."

When Fred said his final thought, he had this look on his face that reminded Terry of Prickard's expression when confronted with racial questions. Terry stayed in his office that night until he finished writing about what had transpired. There was no need for screaming. The spirit was already active. Terry wrote about that face. When Terry finished writing, it was four o'clock in the morning, but he didn't care. He knew he had written a good passage. It became his favorite.

Chapter 25
That Face

Terry listened to Dexter's advice to document Dr. Prickard's actions. Everyday after work, Terry would record the day's occurrences. He noticed that after eighteen months, he had written plenty. Terry had the dates, times, and locations of every office occurrence—good or bad.

Christine Collins had received a raise of eight-and-a-half percent. Dr. Prickard lied. Terry found out that all blacks had started at a lower salary and had received lower raises over the course of the twenty years Dr. Prickard had been the director. Dr. Prickard lied. Not once was there more than two blacks at the professional level. Paul Rue was hired at twenty-five thousand dollars per year back in 1985, whereas blacks and females were started off with the same amount in 1995. Rue was the only white male. Tweety had been given two raises within nine months of her first day of employment. She was also hired at twenty-seven thousand dollars, whereas Brenda and Terry were told their salaries were non-negotiable and received no raises until after one year. Dr. Prickard lied. Tweety was now the highest paid assistant director, but she had made no contribution whatsoever to the office. Marcha was hired without a formal interview, and she was given an extra thousand dollars on her salary. She received two raises within her first year and a promotion to associate director after two years of work. One of Brenda's and Terry's predecessors was a black woman who worked for an eleven-year stretch. She left the job as the assistant director because she never received a promotion. Prickard said that she needed a master's degree. Ms. Donaldson, a Prickard gang member, had been promoted to associate director without ever doing public speaking and no master's degree, but she received two raises within a year. Marcha was promoted without her master's degree. Dr. Prickard lied again. Terry took the entire weekend to organize his material. He took out the yellow pages and prayed for the right attorney.

Terry called Debra Reed, a good ol' southern girl with a slow drawl. Terry took his work journal to their first appointment.

One week later, the attorney called. "Mr. Foster, based upon your complaint, your journal and the preliminary interview, we feel that you definitely have a case."

Terry put his hands to his head to wipe the perspiration away. "I knew it," he said aloud.

During the second appointment, the attorney asked, "Have you suffered any from this discrimination?"

"Well, I haven't slept much, and I've been getting headaches, and I've had gastric problems."

"Do you have any receipts for doctors bills and so forth?"

"Some."

"What else have you done to cope with the discrimination you felt."

"Nothing else, really."

Then Terry remembered. "I started writing to get over this. It was either hit this man or write about hitting him. I prayed for him and hit him on paper."

"Do you have some writings with you?"

"Yeah, here is the first prose I wrote after Prickard figured I knew he was racist. He had a look on his face. I wrote this one that night."

Debra picked up the journal and started reading.

It was deathly quiet for two minutes as her eyes ran from margin to margin. Her eyes filled with water. The prose tore into her soul like Prickard tore into Terry's dreams. She looked at Terry, smiling through her tears.

"This is real good. I know what you're writing about, Mr. Foster. It reminds me of a Norman Rockwell painting. The faces in the painting had the face you described here.

"I can tell you that this man really did hurt you. I feel it and see it in every line you wrote.

Terry just looked at this lady and smiled. He knew he could get Prickard. He knew she would do everything to beat Prickard.

Terry decided to take his time with pursuing the case and allow Prickard and his gang members to make another mistake.

Patience knows all answers.

Prickard went away on a vacation summer weekend, and when he returned, he approached Terry. I heard that you went to the Equal Employment Opportunity Commission Officer."

"How did you know that?"

"People talk, Terry."

Terry then replied, "Don't worry. I'll be meeting with some attorneys off campus next time."

There was a lot to consider. Terry would have to work in this environment while the lawsuit was ongoing. He would have to take a chance of his reputation being destroyed. He would have to come up with the money if the decision was not favorable. Not to mention he would have to go through the EEOC to get permission to sue. *Why should I need permission?* he thought.

The statute of limitations, the order of records, the unknown rules of a right-to-work state all favored Prickard. The lawyer, Debra Reed, told Terry to go to the EEOC office to get the permission to sue. She also said, "There is a strong chance that you have a case. The EEOC office, however, is the most inefficient operation in the world. It is understaffed and poorly funded, because of its importance to black people. They are slow and incompetent until you get to the top representatives."

Terry did as he was told. He dealt with the aforementioned problems of the EEOC. After three weeks, he was able to get an appointment with a top representative, Mrs. Erica Charles.

Mrs. Charles knew her laws and regulations very well. She was very intelligent and frank, unlike her subordinates. After reviewing Terry's case, she decided that under state law Prickard could do anything he wanted. If he wanted to give Terry a one-penny raise and give a white girl a fifty percent raise, then he could because the right-to-work state considers that fair. If he has a track record of underpaying black people and decided to grant one black person a token raise, then according to the law, he did not discriminate. The law ignores the fact that a racist can maneuver things to cover his actions. The law overlooks the fact that although racism is stupid, the individual may be smart enough to create immunity within a system by being nice once. In other words, if a person commits a crime everyday for twenty years and decides to be nice for one day, the law says there are no grounds to take this person to jail.

The EEOC did come up with a strategy. If Terry and Brenda could get all of the blacks before them to verify the data, they would probably have a case. Terry couldn't believe what she was saying. His options were a class action suit, or deal with this blatant discrimination, and/or find a new job. Terry could not believe that he was in that position.

Terry was mentally and physically drained for several days before he and Brenda took the advice to get the class action lawsuit underway.

Part Eight

A Dose of Reality

Chapter 26
Man's Love Hunt

Terry had been in many relationships with wonderful women, and he enjoyed every one of them. But he did not find another love like Queva. The last thing on Terry's mind was falling in love again. He made sure that his feelings never got out of control. He had become stubborn in showing his feelings for anyone. With Queva approaching marriage, Melanie with a boyfriend, and Veronica too far away, Terry had no escape.

Women came and went. Terry was always brutally honest with them. Meesha, a beautiful flight attendant, asked Terry if he thought they would ever become more than bed partners. Terry looked at her and said, "Hey, I am physically attracted and mentally pleased with you, but I don't see a long future with you right now. For right now, I don't feel that I will ever be married to you or anyone else unless you put the root on me or something."

"Damn, Tee, you could show a little bit of consideration. Maybe I like you more than you know. Maybe I am the one for you. Why are you so damn hard?"

"I don't want to leave you hoping and thinking that I'm going to change overnight. The most important thing for me is not to lead you on. If you want me to lie, then I will."

"Naw, you're right, Tee. I was just hoping that things would get serious."

The pause was cold and brittle.

"Is it me, Terry? Am I the reason? Am I pushy? Overweight? Boring? What is it?"

"Meesha, it's me." It was the typical answer he'd given dozens of times when he didn't want the woman. "I think I know how love is supposed to feel, and I'm not there yet." Terry wondered if it would ever come again.

"News flash Tee, just imagine that I am waiting at the airport with tickets in hand. Our flight leaves soon. Are you flying with me?"

Terry rolled over and kissed her on the forehead. They excited each other for the final time. She tried her best to convince Terry that she was the one. He noticed the effort, and while he did love the techniques, he didn't fall in love with her. Two weeks later, the airplane left with Meesha on it, and Terry missed the flight. He thought, *I hope there is a return flight or a layover.* Terry spoke with her on and off for a couple of weeks, but what they had fizzled. He figured. *It would be a year or so before they get together again, and that was fine with him.*

When time permitted Terry searched for Ms. Right. The nightclubs were full of beautiful women who were hungry for attention or yearning for fun. The atmosphere was something that Terry had been accustomed to throughout college. Terry was burned out on nightclubs. Many of the women were looking for the millionaire pro athlete or business tycoon or loaded drug dealer with a fancy car, gold chains, and money to spend. Terry longed to entertain his woman like a rich man. Subconsciously, he compared every woman he met to Veronica or Queva. If Terry found Ms. Right he'd do his best to spoil her like a rich man. Then he thought realistically, *I'd have to spoil her with my charm not my wallet.*

Athletes and businessmen, even a few drug dealers had always spoiled Veronica because she was a beautiful lady. Men fell at her feet. She could walk in a mall for an hour and receive five propositions and five numbers. Veronica always handled herself very well. She desired someone special, unique, and different in his approach.

Terry did not talk with Veronica for almost two weeks due to the busy time of the recruiting year. Terry traveled to a new city every day and Veronica worked a part-time job as a late night telephone operator. The last time they spoke she told Terry she had a surprise for him. When Terry finally got home and regrouped, he called late that Sunday night. The Washington, DC number she gave him had been disconnected. The new number was in North Carolina. Terry quickly dialed the new number, and she picked up.

"Hello."

"Hello, is Veronica available?"

"This is she."

"This is Terry. What's up?"

"It's about time you called."

"Ah. Take it easy, Veronica."

"I needed you all week to help me move. I called twice and left a message. Did you check your messages?"

"No. I haven't checked them for the last couple of days." Terry replied somberly.

"Well that explains my predicament. Are you okay?"

"Yeah." Terry answered

"Well, you need to get over here and help me unpack, Mr. Foster."

Terry didn't hesitate. "Okay."

He got the directions and was off to Veronica's.

He rang the doorbell. She answered the door. She smiled and gave him a hug. Terry walked into her new apartment and said, "Whew, you've got a lot of stuff to unpack. It's going to take a few weeks."

She laughed. "You're right about that. Would you like a pizza?"

Terry and Veronica started talking and working, and before he knew it was four o'clock in the morning. He slept on the futon, and several hours later, she made him breakfast before sending him home to dress for work.

A comforting feeling came over him that day, and everything about life became crystal clear.

Crystal Clear

A touch from your hands
Soothes my aching desires
No blemish
No clouds in your world
Your love is crystal clear

Calm winds whisper tunes of love
Flowers dance to the presence of your smile
I fall into your world
And my life is crystal clear

If you are in my arms
I feel your warmth
If you are on my mind
I am stronger.
When our paths cross
I can see where I am going
Because our love is crystal clear

Lonely nights are extinct
And morning dews freshen yesterdays
Today's glory is shiny and new
Because we are together
And our love is crystal clear
Our love is crystal clear

Chapter 27
I'm Not Ready

After Queva informed Terry about her wedding plans, he realized what she really wanted in life. She wanted stability, security, and a family. She wanted to make a team and play the game of life and win. She wanted an honorable man who would take on problems and share their wealth with children she would die for. She wanted a love that would last forever. Queva longed for the respect of family members, friends, and associates who could look at her family as the perfect example of how someone should exist. She wanted to be able to stand tall in her community as a pillar of strength for those who were less fortunate. She wanted to turn gray in her church as a mother, grandmother, wife, and missionary that God ordained. Queva wanted to be associated with a family of her on creation. She wanted her life to have substance and longevity; she simply wanted to live life right.

Terry felt that Queva needed a strong man to handle her uncanny wit. Queva was also pretty hard on any man's wallet. She would need a husband that was willing to give her a paycheck. Queva loved to shop. For a moment Terry entertained the thoughts that he could satisfy all of her desires. Terry thought for a moment that marriage to Queva would be a soothing, yet adventurous, challenge to succeed. Terry would catch himself wallowing in moments of victory as Queva and he overcame the dreaded past and forgave each other for the pain they caused each other. He dreamed of a new beginning.

Terry pictured them building an intangible castle. That mental castle would be built on a foundation of trust, love, hope and God. A mixture of the dirt and stones they once threw at each other and their enemies, as well, along with the sweat, blood, and tears that came with the package as a result of their immature actions towards each other would make up the brick and cement. The walls would be formed from bricks laid by their hard-working hands. Over time the walls would harden and become smooth from the winds of marriage.

Queva would have her dream rooms, from kitchen to sunroom, which she built herself. And Terry would have his rooms. There would be baby rooms, toy rooms, and guest halls with elaborate furnishings, the rewards from doing for the community, the church, and each other.

The castle would be protected from the elements because God was a roof over their heads. And when there was doubt, sin, or too much pride, the weather would be felt. They would pray to quickly heal their roof. The Lord watched them, and they watched the Lord.

Terry would have liked this castle with any woman. He was not ready to run to Queva and stop her wedding, but he found solace in using the love they had for each other as a measuring stick. Terry knew that he could never trust her again. If there was ever a time he loved, that was on the day he built a mental castle with his Queva.

If Terry had had this frame of mind early in their relationship, Terry would be ready to face the commitment with Queva. But she cheated on him and changed his outlook on life. Terry was not ready to accept the responsibilities of becoming a twosome that women live for.

The single life was something to relish. It was a selfish existence, which featured independence and freedom, along with one's personal property and no stress from a nagging counterpart. On nights when he wanted to entertain, he would invite a date over. If he wanted his friends to stay over late, he was the only decision-maker. It was all in his control. There were few worries. Even if a lady came promising that he could still have a quasi-single life, Terry refused her offer because of any strings that might be attached.

After dreaming of a castle with Queva and weighing the pros of the single life, Terry thought, *I'm not ready for the married life, and I'm growing tired of the single life. Now what am I to do?*

Terry was a fruit ready for the picking. He was deeply enthralled by Veronica. Spending time with her was his favorite time of the day. There were few worries and little pressure about marriage, settling down, and commitment. Terry was free to go where he wanted, free to see who he wanted, and free to disappear if he wanted, and it was the same for Veronica. Every woman he came across made an issue about his freedoms. Veronica was definitely giving Terry his space, time, and peace of mind. Terry felt as though sooner or later the pressure would come. Terry thought about marriage and felt that it was not necessarily Veronica herself that made him want to marry. She may have simply been lucky enough to be in his life at the time he was ripened for the picking. This worried Terry because he didn't want to just settle for anyone. He wanted to make sure she was the one.

Part Nine

Terry's Purpose in Life

Chapter 28
The Purpose

Terry enjoyed her company, her beauty, and he respected her as though she were his mother. Terry appreciated her not mentioning his outburst in her new church. He knew if things kept going as they were, he would end up marrying this girl. The couple found themselves doing movies, going to parks, exercising, having lunch and dinner together, and most important, going to church together.

Terry met Reverend Wilson and talked with him on several occasions. Reverend Wilson was a true servant with God in his heart. He had an attitude that commanded respect and devotion. Terry felt like he had another brother when he spent time with Reverend Wilson. Reverend Wilson felt the same way. Three months after they had known each other, Reverend Wilson asked Terry about the first time he came to his church. He said, "I know there is something special about you because when you stood up, you spoke in tongues."

Terry said, "Naw! I said, 'Lord, have mercy,' Reverend."

"No, Terry, you spoke in tongues."

"To be honest with you, I said, 'Lord have mercy'. You heard a nervous brother experiencing the Holy Ghost for the first time."

"I have it on videotape. You spoke in tongues."

Terry gazed into the reverend's eyes and saw his confidence.

"Okay, I may have."

"We need to meet in my office one day to study the bible."

"Yeah. Okay." Terry said eagerly.

"What about next week? Tuesday, around six o'clock."

"Reverend Wilson, I'll see you there."

On Tuesday, Terry walked into the reverend's office with bible in hand. The preacher greeted him with a handshake and hug. They sat down and Reverend Wilson opened the door to his credenza. Terry looked at him and said, "I don't need to see it."

"Don't be afraid, Terry. Trust me, I have seen more fake ones than real ones. This will be good for you."

Terry looked at his experience with his hand covering his mouth. He heard his cry out to the Lord. He listened to the sound and said, "Play it again, Reverend." The reverend rewound the tape stopped and pressed play again. Terry couldn't believe it. "I don't know what I said. I know what I felt, I don't know what was said."

"Don't panic Terry. You are very special, my friend, you are very special. Have you every felt this way before?"

"No, not really."

"Not really? Terry, what's this not really?"

"Well, it was like I lost consciousness, but I knew what I was doing. The feeling just seemed beyond control. And it happened when I didn't want it to."

"I don't understand, Terry. What do you mean by not really?"

"I meditate on a regular basis. I write the feelings I have during meditation down on paper. I am conscious but not totally in control of my body and mind. I hear screams or directed voices that tell me what to write down or what to do about a situation. After a couple of hours, I stop hearing screams and the writing stops. Sometimes I end up with stories, poetry, and sometimes scribble-scrabble, sometimes nothing. Whatever I get helps me through the day."

"Terry, I want you to tape the next time you decide to meditate."

"I call it screaming, similar to dreaming. You see dreams; I hear screams, no images involved."

"Well, the next time you scream, please tape it." The reverend dug into his desk drawer and handed him the hand-held voice-activated tape recorder.

"I will!"

"I want you to read over a few bible verses before you scream, okay?"

"No problem, Doctor Reverend Deacon Wilson."

They laughed and Terry went home, anxious to read what had been given to him to study.

Terry read from the bible verses listed and attempted to scream. He did his normal routine and wrote a short poem. He used the recorder, but it recorded nothing except the movement of the ink pen on paper. He took the tape recorder back to Reverend Wilson. Reverend Wilson agreed that maybe there was nothing to record. Reverend Wilson took the recorder and dropped it in his desk. Terry told him if there was anything he could do, just call him.

"Yeah, Terry, I have one question. Is there anyone else in your family that can scream?"

"My great-grandmother used to do it. My grandmother knows a lot about what happened. We came across this quilt that has been in the family for a long time. I screamed one day and got a list of names, and on that same day, Grandma was stitching some of the names in that quilt. I fainted when I saw what was happening. That's when she told me I was special, but this had nothing to do with talking in tongues."

"Have you talked to her lately?"

"No."

"Well, next Friday, let's go down there to the boonies of South Carolina and talk to your grandma. We'll get back here in time for choir rehearsal."

"Hey, I'll ask Veronica if she wants to go."

"Yeah, great idea."

177

Reverend Wilson sat back in his chair and thought about his unusual friend, Terry Foster. He then thought, *Lord, have mercy. He is special.*

Friday came around, and the three of them left Raleigh on the four-hour trip to Georgetown, South Carolina. Terry drove the entire way home while Veronica slept. The reverend kept talking about how thick the woods were in this part of South Carolina. He was teasing Terry about the fact that Terry was a country boy. Terry bragged and said, "At least I know something about good country food and country living." As the car turned on the last stretch before his grandma's house, the preacher read the sign, *Welcome to Sampit.* He laughed and said, "Sam's Pit !"

Terry replied, "Sampit, no pause. No possessive. Sampit."

"Terry, you're from Sampit, not Georgetown. Ha! Ha! If that ain't the country, I don't know what is."

Terry bragged, "Once you stay a little while, you'll want to come back." Veronica and Reverend Wilson laughed. Terry said to Veronica, "Go back to sleep, sleepy head. I've got enough problems with your preacher teasing me. I don't need you laughing, too."

The car erupted in more laughter.

"Welcome to Sampit." Terry bragged. "You'll never be the same."

Terry's grandma was happy to see Terry. She was even happier to see Veronica. She thought the preacher was going to marry her grandson off. She said, "Reverend, this ain't a house for a wedding." The reverend smirked and said, "I'll marry anywhere you want me to." Everyone laughed. Terry said, "Alright, Grandma, let's not scare Veronica off."

Laughter rang throughout the house. Uncles and aunts came to see Terry and his friends. The Foster clan had a cookout planned for Saturday afternoon, so everyone was stopping by. The preacher stayed at the house while Veronica and Terry went visiting his friends and to see his parents.

Terry still had the key for his parent's house. He turned the lock and entered through the front door. Terry's mom said, "Look at what the devil sent here, Joe. It's Terry and his new girlfriend." Terry hugged his mom and kissed her and then he went to hug his father, who said, "Boy! Now, that's a pretty girl you got on your side. Just like your Uncle Jesse."

Veronica smiled and hugged him, "Nice to meet you, Mr. Foster." Terry's dad took her by the hand and said, "Sit down here. Let me see if you should break up with my big head boy." She sat and got acquainted with the old man as Terry and his mom talked about his dad.

Terry asked, "The old man's arm has not changed since Uncle Jesse's murder, huh?"

"Yeah his right arm is still stiff and deformed. But his spirit is good. God is good to let me keep him for a little while longer."

"He sure is, Mama."

"Is he still having those bad nightmares?"

"Lord! Tee, he has them every night. It almost like he's a run away slave."

"He'll never get caught, Mama. He'll never get caught."

Terry and his father sat up and drank some good liquor while Mama spent time talking to Veronica. Terry was happy to see his Mama and Veronica get off to a good start. When Terry's parents went to get ready for bed, Veronica and Terry stepped outside to go for a walk.

The midnight moon was beautiful. The cloudless skies made the white sand of the dirt road leading to the house visible. They walked and talked. Terry looked at her and said, "You know what, I guess you are my girlfriend."

She said, "Is that your way of asking me?"

"Veronica, will you be my queen, my girlfriend?" Terry was very serious.

"Are you serious?" She asked.

"Yes?"

"Then I have to say no."

"What?"

"No."

"Damn! Okay, okay what is a man to do with you?"

"Terry, I don't want to be your girlfriend, I want to be your wife."

Terry stepped back to look into her eyes.

"We've been dating for a long time. You were my boyfriend from the day we went to church and you caught the Holy Ghost." She snickered.

"That's probably why I caught the Holy Ghost. That's still a sensitive subject with me. Don't laugh."

Veronica then said, "Let's keep our relationship simple. No titles, but intentions. If you intend to marry me, then we won't need to be girlfriend or boyfriend. Those boyfriend/girlfriend arrangements are just an excuse for people to have sex. I'd rather be married first."

Veronica leaned forward and kissed Terry for the first time. They embraced and kissed for several moments. He said to himself, *"She's good. A little crazy, but good."*

The couple held hands all the way back to the house. When Veronica took her shower, Terry called his grandmother's house to see how the preacher was handling country living. Grandma answered the phone.

"Hey Grandma, How are y'all doing over there?"

"Fine, Tee! I'm teaching the preacher a few things. He loves my biscuits and syrup."

"Let me talk to him, Grandma."

"Hey, Terry, this is a wonderful lady. She and your aunts have me feeling like I am family."

"That's great. Just don't eat all of my biscuits."

"Too late. I left you one. I know it's late, Terry, but we need to talk. Can you come over right now?"

"Yeah, I'll be there in a few minutes. Don't eat my biscuit."

When Terry entered the house, his grandma motioned at her favorite chair and said, "Terry, sit down, baby." Grandma sat on the couch adjacent to Terry and then said, "The reverend tells me that you spoke in tongues the first time you went to his church."

Terry smirked, "Yes ma'am."

Grandma smiled then whispered, "Your great grandmother did the same thing."

"Yeah, really, so what does this mean?" Terry replied.

"Terry, your grandma and I think that you are a special one who can interpret tongues also." The reverend eagerly interjected his comments.

"Grandma, it happened only once."

"Baby, I want you to read Corinthians, chapters thirteen and fourteen and let us know what you think."

"Right now?" Terry was reluctant.

"Boy, read the thing, before I..." She raised her hand.

"Yes Ma'am." Tee laughed.

Reverend Wilson snickered like a little kid.

Terry took the bible in the den and read the chapters. He began reluctantly, but after seeing himself in the passages, he was eager to finish reading the chapter.

He finished the chapter, sat back, and said to himself, *I don't believe this.* Terry picked up a pen and pad from by the phone, held the bible under his forearm, and tried to scream. After about ten minutes, he heard his grandma and Reverend Wilson talking about his great-grandmother and himself. At the exact point that Terry fell into his deep meditation, Terry heard his grandmother mention the Holy Ghost in her conversation with the reverend. Terry was concentrating on Corinthians, chapter fourteen and the discussions of prophecy and tongues. Terry went into a trance. His legs were shaking, his free hand gripped the arm of the chair, and his mouth was open. For the first time in meditation, he spoke in tongues. His body went into convulsions. The reverend heard the commotion and walked toward the den. To his surprise, he saw Terry's expressions. He knew immediately that Terry was screaming.

The reverend sat on the couch and reached into his pocket for his recorder. He pressed play as Terry spoke. He left for a quick second to get the grandmother to witness. She came and sat down, a look of complete amazement on her face. Terry squirmed, grunted, and clicked his tongues and lips, his face had a look of pain. Every few seconds he would write down what he was experiencing.

Unbeknownst to his observers, Terry had spoken with the Holy Ghost or an angel, he wasn't sure which. The spirit reached out and touched Terry's hand. His spirit took the angel's hand and walked to a light so bright that Terry felt the energy. Then Terry's head lifted, and his eyes opened without a word. The reverend and his grandma knew that Terry was experiencing something. Terry was barely breathing. The reverend became frightened and took his hand to pray. Terry's hand was cold. The reverend went to feel his pulse and found out that Terry's heartbeat was extremely slow. The reverend had felt this feeling many times before by the sick beds of people waiting to die.

Terry heard a familiar voice. "Tee, Boy I was wondering when you would figure out how to get here. Terry, in a few seconds, your spirit will see my spirit." Terry thought, Uncle Jesse.

"It's me boy, it's me."

"I miss you, man."

"I miss you too, Tee!"

Uncle Jesse then said, "We have little time before you return. The angel that you touched was your great grandmother. She is the one who has given you the gift of screaming." Terry looked at his hands and saw that this lady was still holding his hand. He looked into her eyes and felt her love immediately. "She has helped you to get to this point. She's your guardian angel."

Tee smiled and said, "You're the usher in the church. You're the familiar old lady in the church."

She said, "I'm only one-hundred-and-eighty years old, darling."

"Bless you, grandma, bless you." Terry replied with a big smile.

Uncle Jesse then said, "Hey, I want you to tell your dad to stop worrying about me. I'm okay. Let him know that those cops got something hot coming. He needs to release that anger. Tell him I'm with Sharna on the beach listening to Louis Armstrong. He'll believe you then; he'll know that I'm okay. Tell him to go to Dr. Kreik on 227 North East Avenue, New York to get his shoulder fixed almost like new. I got about a half a million dollars on the stock market now. Tell him to open and read my mail. It's all his now. Also, tell Mama I love her.

"Oh yeah, if you're wondering why Sharna is familiar to you, she's the lady I fell in love with in college. She died of breast cancer in our senior year. Your dad thought we should have married. I always wanted to, but she knew she would die, so we never got married. You heard my scream a couple of years ago. You wrote, *I Feel Proud to be with Louis.* You heard my wishes to be with Sharna when she died in my arms over twenty-five years ago. I screamed to the top of my lungs. Now, we listen to Louis everyday."

Terry could only say, "Wow!"

Terry we have only a few minutes left, Grandma has to talk to you now, so pay attention. Terry nodded in agreement.

"Hey sugar, make sure you tell that daughter of mine I miss her." Terry couldn't speak. She was the spitting image of the picture on the mantle.

"Baby Tee, you're able to experience screaming because you have a purpose. The last thing you want to do is explain what your body is saying or writing to the reverend. He is overly eager to find out things that neither he nor his followers are ready to handle. When you return, you must destroy the tapes and the pad."

"Yes Ma'am," Terry said like a soldier. His great grandma smiled and continued speaking.

"A couple of months ago, you heard names of people from your family's past. You and my baby did the right things by putting the names on the blanket. Those names are to go before Lord Jesus when judgement day comes. These are the people that will go through Heaven's door. We are witnesses for them. They are special people that have saved our lives or have just been good to us. Make sure that every worthy name is sewn in that quilt. If anyone brings you a name, scream about the name and the person who brought the name to see if they are worthy.

"Also baby, please marry soon; I like the girl you are dating. But honey, remember that any woman you love and pray with will be a good wife. You just have to select her. All women thoroughly immersed in the Lord are great to marry. As the man in the relationship, you must make sure that your spirits stay in contact with the Holy Ghost, the comforter. Then there are no problems that cannot be solved."

"I like this Veronica gal, too. If you don't marry her, the reverend will be happier because he has a crush on Veronica. One of you proud men will be her husband. It's up to you, Tee, to determine if you are compatible." Uncle Jesse said with excitement.

"Terry, make sure you pray and keep screaming and meditating with the Lord by your side." His great grandma said with a stern face.

"You have to go now." She whispered softly. "We will never see you again in this lifetime, but if you live your life right, you will still hear our screams. But you'll never see us again in this form."

"Yes ma'am!"

"Make sure you get back to Heaven, Tee." Uncle Jesse replied.

"I love you Terry, stay strong."

"I love you too, man."

"Tee, take care of everyone, and tell your dad. Don't forget."

The great-grandmother returned to her spirit form and took Terry by the hand. Terry turned to look at Uncle Jesse. Uncle Jesse waved goodbye from the gate of Heaven and started singing his favorite song, *At the gate I know.*

Terry sang with him. He shed a tear and waved goodbye with his free hand.

The angel kissed him on the forehead and repeated her instructions. "Tee, destroy the tapes and the pad. Tell the reverend he holds the answers in his heart, not in the tapes."

The reverend noticed Terry's spirit return.

The recorder had been running for twelve minutes. Terry came to as though he had been asleep for hours. Grandma was shocked and placed a cold towel on the back of his neck.

Terry got up grabbed the tape recorder and his pad.

"What are you doing, Terry?" The reverend said frantically.

Terry placed his hand on his shoulders and said, "You hold the answers in your heart. I have to destroy this cassette as well as the VCR tape of the church service."

The reverend kneeled and thanked the Lord in prayer.

Grandma was afraid. Terry told her the purpose of the names and the quilt. He also told her that her mama sent her love and so did Uncle Jesse. Grandma fell to her knees and praised Him with tearful eyes.

Terry went back to his parent's house to wake his dad. He told him everything. His dad would have his first worry-free sleep since Uncle Jesse's murder. Dad looked up to the skies and said, "Brother Jesse, I knew you would marry , I knew you would." Terry and the old man hugged each other and laughed. "Boy, we got some money now, but I'd give it all back to spend one minute with Mama and Jesse."

Terry said, "There isn't enough money to pay for one second, Dad."

Terry then went towards Veronica's bedroom wearing a big grin. Veronica slept with the sweetest smile. He looked at the moon and sent a silent prayer to be together.

Terry read the scribble he wrote and deciphered the one message he understood. It was about Uncle Jesse... *Life Went Home Today?* Then he destroyed the tapes and the pad. The drinks he and his dad had earlier and the late night screaming had him drained. Terry finally got to sleep at five o'clock in the morning.

Inspiration # 18 July 5, 1983

Life Went Home Today?

Life went home today
And I was not ready to live with death
Grief and shock brought many tears
My eyes won't get any rest

Life went home a few days ago
And I was not ready to fill your grave
Looking at the future without you
Makes its harder to be brave

Life went home a few weeks ago
And I was not ready to compromise
I go to sleep in the daytime
Crying at night, asking God, "Why? Why?"

Life went home a month ago
And I was not ready to accept the transformation
There is one way to contact you
I must pray and keep the dedication

Life went home a year ago
And I was not ready to relive that day
But the memories of being with you
Made joy overcome pain with subtle delay

Life went home a few years ago
And I am ready; our memories are still fresh
I've learned to laugh without you
I guess I survived God's test

Life went home a long time ago
And I remember you like it was yesterday
It's amazing how time heals the heart
It's amazing how Life never went away!

Chapter 29
Professional Development

Terry's first summer in this position proved to have some professional development rewards. Terry flew to Seattle to attend the National Association of Minority Admission Counselors' (NAMAC) conference. Groups teamed together to evaluate, discuss, and solve problems or issues dealing with minority students and the issues minority recruiters face in their profession.

Many of his peers faced the same problems and had the same complaints. In casual talk, Terry found out that many of his peers were underpaid. It was even mentioned that many newcomers would be forced out of their jobs due to salary, working conditions, or the most common reason: discrimination. Many didn't go to the conference because of funding, scheduling, or fear of getting a reputation as a aggressive minority, but Terry knew after his first year that he would go again, and possibly every year of his career.

On the very last night, there was a banquet where people received rewards and prizes for the extra efforts. The teams that worked together all week had to do a skit together. Some people were invited to display their singing, poetry and musical talents. Terry wanted to recite one of his poems, but he didn't have the confidence or material that would carry well on stage. His group did a skit about the various group leaders.

When he returned to Wolfe State, he felt like he left family back in Seattle. He became depressed because he had to go back to a depressing situation. He wished that he could bring about ten people to work with him.

When Prickard asked Terry about the conference, Terry told him it was the best experience that he had ever had.

The following year Terry and Brenda left for NAMAC held at Hampton University. Brenda had been to the conference while working with another school. She knew the benefits of being with peers, networking strategies, and most importantly, relaxing away from the office. This was Terry's second time. They both knew what to expect.

Unlike Terry's first conference, this one more specifically addressed Terry's and Brenda's problems. That year's teams had to do another skit. After three days of tossing ideas around, Terry told them, "I have an idea." He dug into his bag and pulled out the prose he wrote while in Sampit. They read the poem, and one group member said, "I would have never thought you were this talented. This is a great piece." The group leader read it and said "It's final. This is our skit." They voted, and, before they knew it, a mini-production was completed.

Terry was nervous because he had just opened his writing to the public. He also had to recite it. The group added great ideas to the skit and after 20 minutes of practice, everyone had their parts.

Time for the talent portion of the banquet quickly came. Everyone in Terry's group sat at tables strategically placed throughout the audience. All the acts were great, but Tee's group had a different style. The group leader grabbed the microphone and signaled for the dimming of the lights. She said to the packed auditorium, "Everyone, we have a skit we want to perform. In order for this skit to work, you must close your eyes and lay your heads back. Everyone please do this now." When everyone had laid their heads back, the skit started.

Terry stood from his table, nervous but strong. He started the skit just like it came to him in his scream.

I can hear their cries. That's why I fight for my rights

The five group members stood at their tables and said:

Those murdered by ancient hands
Scream from unmarked graves every night.

Terry then said:

I can hear the roots shaking on my family tree
I can hear a healing body whisper

'One day they won't do my peoples the way they do me'

Can you hear your ancestors' screams?
Can you imagine your ancestors' dreams?
The pain they felt was a three-hundred-year flood
And today's sores of life still bleed their blood

It's not a mystery to us anymore
As a government covers up, they scream louder
I can't ignore!
They scream

Then Dejuna, a beautiful African-American princess, spoke in her best African accent. To Terry's ears, she sounded like his guardian angel.

No leaf should go unturned
No clue should be overlooked
And always have faith in the good book

Rafina, with her schoolbook in hand, acting like a teacher, said:

Even when great changes have occurred
And things should never be the same
One should never look left without looking right again

Carl then said his piece just like Uncle Jesse sounded.

Don't forget where you come from
Don't forget where you been
Don't forget ancestors, don't let the evil win

Take pride in what you have regardless of its value
Remember millions died so you can have a choice
Don't lose this battle

Terry then said:

My ancestors are still crying, I can hear them say.
'One day my peoples will learn how to read and write.
One day they will get equal pay.'

Lavonna said with an business woman's tone:

All of those graves still scream for justice
Remember, even though the crosses burn less
Does not mean they trust us!

In our world there is no such thing as fair play
We need to be concerned with judgment day!

Tracy then walked through the audience, saying and motioning:

Now, lay your head back and close your eyes
Feel your soul move, feel your ancestors drive
They never gave up, and because you are living, they never died
You can hear them screaming, telling us how to stay alive

Finally, every group member went to each table and motioned to them and said:

Lay your head back and close your eyes
If you can hear your ancestors, then you will surely Survive!
Lay your head back and close your eyes

After a short silence, Terry finished the skit, saying:

When you hear a scream, always remember to keep God by your side

The crowd went crazy with applause. Some people actually felt their souls move. They had been awed by this skit.

Terry had never been more proud of his writing. The master of ceremonies took the microphone and said, "Where did y'all find that poem?" The group leader answered, "Terry Foster wrote it and the group produced it." The emcee then said, "Please give them another round of applause. That was one of the best skits I've experienced."

Terry felt very good about how the skit was received. He decided to share his favorite writing with the audience. Terry placed his name on the list for additional acts. He opened up to the audience and told them what inspired this selection. He talked about his director's wicked ways. He let them know how his lawyer shed a tear and how his father cried when he read it after the attack that resulted in the death of his brother.

Terry had the audience ready. He recited *That Face* publicly.

190

That Face!

Have you seen that face?
I have seen that face
But not as direct and as frightening
As in the past!

I have read about you many times
You are synonymous with Satan and Beelzebub
Your countenance is invisible to the untrained eye
But I have seen you before!

That Face can come in the form
Of a smile, a frown, a grit, a wink, or no expression at all
When delivered
And That Face can come in the form
Of a smile, a frown, a tear, shock
Anger, or no expression at all
When received

Regardless of who delivers or receives
Its origin is the coldest winds
This Universe and the human body
Have ever known!

That Face was mastered
And born in the USA

I have seen that face on my sisters and brothers
Colleagues, comrades, enemies, family, strangers,
Employers, white, black, red and yellow
I have seen That Face!

When you participated, witnessed, avoided, escaped
Laughed, cried or read about, bled and died
Because of the lynching, burning, beating
And cold murder of black men

When you viewed, used or read about, the white only
And colored only signs, the back of the bus
The infamous March to that mountain top
Or when you have said,
Heard, read, written or have been
Somebody's Honky, Nigger, Chink, Spic or Jew

"What did he call me?"

Then and only then,
Has one delivered or received
That FACE

That Face is still embedded in the minds of little white
And black boys and girls
Who grew up in the 30s, 40s, 50s, and 60s
A sense of superiority and control for the white
The sense of inferiority, paranoia, and fear for the black

That Face which has seen and experienced
Jim Crow Still affects my life and it lives today!
When my President, Congressmen, CEO, Director
Employer, Superintendent, Professor, or leader
Who is older than forty-five years of age
Has to make a decision between black and white
He or she uses childhood memories
And without a doubt, That Face appears

One day there will be no one who has
First hand experience with
Beatings lynchings, and Jim Crow

One day there will be fewer
That have had these first-person stories told to them

One day "That Face" will change
One day "That Face" will die
Praise GOD for death!

One day, a new face will appear
It will become unnoticeable to many, but in no way
Will it be as successful as its predecessor

Do you know why?
Because I can still see That old Face!

My brothers and sisters, have you seen That Face?
Do you remember the facial expressions of those who
Delivered or received an -ism?

Yeah! You remember!
Can you see the transformations from old to new?

Oh! Yes!
I know who you are
I remember you!
Regardless of how you change, I can still see
THAT FACE!

And I say unto you,

Praise GOD for death!

When he finished, everyone had felt his pain. The audience, some with tears in their eyes, gave Terry a standing ovation. Terry found another purpose for his life: teaching people how to get closer to their spirits by meditation and screaming and exposing racism. As they cheered, Terry wiped his eyes and came down from the podium, anxious to sit and praise the Lord. His friends and group met him at the side of the stage with hi-fives, hugs, handshakes, and kisses for sharing his work.

On their ride back, the co-workers decided that they would leave Wolfe State. They decided the pain had become too stressful and was not worth the salary.

Chapter 30
Prayer Works

Terry and Veronica were getting closer after she moved to Raleigh. Sometimes they would have arguments, especially over the point that Terry still spoke to old girl friends and acquaintances. They had a friendship that was quickly approaching the time when Terry had to make a decision to get married. Veronica just wanted to be with her man and wanted Tee to be all about her. Veronica had stopped talking to her male friends because the majority of them had the wrong intentions. Veronica made it clear that she was involved with Terry, someone special, but Terry did not inform his friends about the importance of Veronica in his life. As far as Terry was concerned, he had no girlfriend. Veronica was only a really good friend.

During one of these heated discussions Terry asked, "Veronica, do you remember the Thanksgiving weekend before we said our goodbyes? You said, 'Baby, its been a long time since you've done something sweet. Please write me a poem to brighten my day.'

"I didn't hesitate; I said, 'Okay, I'll write it tonight! I've been real busy and stressed over this job, so forgive me please?' Do you remember?"

"Yeah! Terry, I remember!" Veronica replied angrily.

"As you cranked the car to go home, you said, 'Terry, don't worry, everything will be just fine. Remember, I love you baby, have a good day tomorrow!' "

"Then I said, 'I'll be fine. I'm down with you, too, Boo! Take care!'

"In a matter of minutes I began writing how I felt about you. I had finally met someone that could bring true love back into my life. Love seemed like a distant star after many years of being a player.

"I remember when my ex-girlfriends or associates would say, 'I love you!' Usually I'd say, 'I'm down with you, too', or 'Like twin babies.' "

I'd refused to say I love you without meaning it.

"But, Veronica, you're different!"

Veronica impatiently said, "Go ahead, Terry. Finish!"

"Hey! Let me finish! Okay." Terry hurriedly replied.

"Well, on Easter, I asked Grandma to pray for a good woman in my life. Shortly after Grandma's prayers, you called me. When I told Gramps I finally knew that someone, she said, 'Terry, it takes time for people to know that they've been blessed to be together. I prayed for this union. Now, it's up to you to figure out if she was sent by a false prophet or the kingdom of God.'

"I learned two things from that lesson. First, I needed to be patient before I got too serious. Secondly, when old, wise God-fearing people pray for you, things happen!"

Terry expected a response, but Veronica was silent and unsmiling.

"Before all of these problems developed, I expressed how I felt about you. I don't want to be without you, Veronica. You know how I feel about you!"

Veronica looked Terry in the eyes with fury and said "Terry, it's time for you to leave now!"

Terry left without saying another word and refused to call her. He remained on pins and needles for several hours, then he took the phone off the hook. He mailed her some poems to explain.

196

He thought, *I have worried enough. I'll put things in God's hands now.*

Two days later, Veronica called Terry, and in a teary, scratchy voice said, "Terry, these are truly lovely. It took me some time to open the packages."

Terry said, "Thanks!"

She asked, "Where do these words come from?"

Terry quickly answered, "The words come from you. This is how you make my soul feel."

Veronica then said, "If I am this good to you, then why did you find a way to jeopardize everything?"

Terry replied, "I'm not perfect. Anyway, I wanted to be sure. Are you still my daydream?"

Terry could hear her smile through the phone. "I better be!"

Sweetheart: Let's Pray Together

Dear Lord,
Thank you for the answer
We've been waiting for
We asked that question
Not knowing if our words were poor

The answer brought a new meaning
And our lives will never be the same
We will always trust in you, Lord
If any doubt rises again!

It took some time and obstacles to see your gift
Now we kneel before your throne
Its amazing how things work if we just pray
You will hear our every groan

The answer to our questions was a resounding YES
Not a word was spoken
But we knew we had been blessed
Obviously, the glow from our angels' halos made us know
That it's okay to marry
We only had to ask in prayer
In order to do so

Now we kneel before you
Overjoyed, our eyes filled with tears
Because with your guidance in our lives
Whom shall we fear?

Yes! Now we kneel before you
Giving you your praise to hear
Because with your guidance in our lives
What, when, and whom shall we fear?
Thank you Lord! Amen

Terry went on to say, "God has many ways of showing you the truth. If you decide to marry without his permission, then it is your marriage. And sooner or later, God will show you what your creation without his guidance will yield.

"Infidelity, money, temptations, jealousy, illness, insecurity, distance, incompatibility, mental and physical abuse, everydayness, stress, lack of friendship and lack of direction will push your marriage into divorce or separation and you and your partner into debt, jail, or even death.

"In today's climate, many couples forget the true meaning of togetherness. There are many marriages that lack the foundation that is needed in order to survive. Many couples have love for each other, but very few survive without loving God and giving Him praise. With God on our side what, when and whom shall we fear? God is amazing! We need to take time to know him!"

Veronica smiled and said. "Amen!"

Chapter 31
Darryl Johnson

It was exactly twenty days before Terry was about to leave his post as assistant director. He found a job with a private sector organization that was willing to double his salary. He had to take this job. He didn't tell Prickard; he only spoke to Brenda. He had just finished typing his resignation letter when a knock at the door startled him.

It was Darryl Johnson, the student who started everything for Terry; the student who taught Terry that the I-am-greater-than-thou complex must end and begin at certain times of one's life. Darryl had come by to deliver a gift. He had gone to community college and brought back two years of straight A's. He had earned his associate's degree. Terry got up and hugged him.

"I'm proud of you man. I'm proud."

He replied. "Me, too."

Terry said, "Take that hat off."

"Oh, I'm sorry," Darryl laughed.

"Hey man, you look the same, but you're thinking different nowadays."

"Yes sir."

"I know you're feeling good."

"Yeah. I wanted to drop this application off to you because you really made it happen for me."

Terry smiled. "Did you type it?"

"Of course." Darryl replied.

"Don't worry about the application fee. I'll waive it because of these grades." Terry handed the check back to him.

Darryl said, "Thanks, Mr. Foster."

Terry entered the application into the computer and quickly accepted Darryl into the program of his choice, Electrical Engineering.

"Darryl, you have just been accepted into this college. I hope you remembered what I told you."

"Yeah."

They both said it together, "Keep focused."

Terry made a copy of Darryl's grades and placed it into his journal. The two talked about a few things, then Darryl left the office.

Darryl did not know how much he had helped Terry.

Terry told Darryl, "Thanks."

Terry turned to his computer and deleted his resignation letter.

Chapter 32
No More Crabs in the Bucket

Brenda and Terry were contemplating their decisions. Brenda had found a job but was not ready to move. Terry had had enough. His purpose was already defined, but they were still soldiers in the fight for equity for blacks in this office. Terry had managed to postpone accepting the new job for one more week. He got a call requesting that he and Brenda meet a former black assistant director at a nearby restaurant for lunch. This brother had gone on to become a director at another college.

They greeted each other and walked behind a curtain to a reserved section of the restaurant. To Brenda's and Terry's surprise, there was one white woman, Debra Reed, and all of the former black assistant directors. Attorney Reed, had done her research and called the people two weeks after Terry's disgruntling news from the EEOC. She had worked for six months to get everything straight. She handed Terry a four-hundred page document of everyone's experiences.

Afterwards, they went to issue papers to Prickard. Prickard walked outside to greet Ms. Reed. When he saw all of them, he almost passed out. The attorney read him the paper and told him this lawsuit would be carried out. Prickard's face fell. The lawsuit was going to be for twelve million dollars.

At the end of the day, all the excitement had drained Terry. He just thought about Prickard and how things would be heading toward a big lawsuit. Terry then wondered if

Prickard's name would ever end up on someone's quilt. Terry thought, *One never knows what will tarnish his or her record with the Creator.* Terry tried his best to scream about Prickard's punishment or even his life. Terry went through the regular routine; He laid his head back, kicked his shoes off, and tucked pen and paper firmly under his forearm. Terry could not find a connection with Prickard's soul or spirit in the beginning. But after an entire hour, Terry found one thing on his paper that signified Prickard's journey. Terry's journal had *"HAY"* written in large capital letters. Terry quickly fell to his knees and gave a prayer to look over Prickard and his transgressions. Prickard would never become a needle.

Chapter 33
The Fruit is Ripe

Veronica turned twenty-eight on her birthday. Terry was as excited as a new baby. He wanted to thank Veronica for keeping him happy and answering his prayers. He could not wait to give her a special birthday party and equally special gifts. Terry screamed for hours thinking about the first time he met Veronica and how his life had not been the same since. He wanted to thank her and God for teaching him how to respect women again. Terry was also in love with this woman because they took their time to know each and found out that joy comes in many ways. Terry decided to give her two special poems on her birthday. He presented them to her at his apartment with a candle filled birthday cake, cards and presents.

Terry's screaming expedition took him back to their first meeting but also to his purpose of his endeavors as a young man. Terry handed the first poem to Veronica. He waited patiently as she read the poem titled *It's your Birthday, Again.*

A tear fell from her eye as she read. Veronica knew that Terry had written this poem with his spirit and soul. The other poems he had written for her may have come from screaming but these were the first poems he had written with her true knowledge of his gift. She knew that Terry had given much thought and meditation to put these words on paper. She felt honored to be a focal point of Terry's life. Her tears hit the paper as she looked at Terry. She was overjoyed with happiness and respect for a man who wrote so beautifully and knew his own spirit so well.

It's your birthday again
I've known you for many years

I remember playing with you before we were born
You were my soul-mate in heaven.

I remember you kissing me in kindergarten
I acted like I didn't like you, but I did!

I remember the puppy love games in middle school
The passing of love notes in class, at recess, and in church!

I remember the days we spent with others
Knowing that they were not the ones

I remember prom night, I remember the first time we made love
I remember meeting your family and knowing I belonged

I remember crying because you broke my heart
But I recovered, still searching for you

You were my drive with every failed relationship
You were my reason to go on

Right now, I'm in Heaven again
Because I found my old soul-mate.

It's your birthday again
And I have known you all these years

Terry read his second poem. It held such emotion and dignity that he even became teary-eyed. Terry's voice changed tones as he tried to explain the next poem. He then just said, "Veronica, please listen."

I have been the wolf in sheep's clothing for many women
Satisfying my hunger for your treasures and my pleasures

Out of all of the relationships, I never heard your cry
Until I heard a scream I couldn't justify
I have done too much damage to break another heart
Playing silly games so we would be apart

206

I hope God will forgive me
For the things I have done in the past
He made me hear your voice, He made my barriers crash

A single man is screaming, and she has heard his last breath
Because an overwhelming love has been placed on his chest

This single man has died for a better life
Because the real man within asked,
"Will you be my wife?"

Terry then dug into his pocket and brought out a two-karat emerald-cut, crystal-clear diamond ring. He repeated the final stanza:

The single man has died for a better life,
Because the real man within is asking,
Veronica, will you be my wife?

Veronica was shaking with joy and tears. She said, "Yes. Oh, yes, honey!" She had salty tears spilling over her lips, and her smile reflected every ounce of love a body could hold. She kissed Terry, and they hugged each other all night. Terry had never been prouder and more comfortable than now. The single man had died. He was now ready to be a real man.

As Terry talked about their future, she could only look in bewilderment at the lovely ring. Terry saw the sparkle in her eye and said, "Mrs. Foster, we need to set a date."

She smirked and said, "That's Mrs. Sellers-Foster to you."

Terry gave her a fake frown, and said, "We have to talk about this last name, thing. You see, I still have the receipt for that rock."

They laughed into the night and fell asleep in each other's arms.

After Terry received approval from her parents, six months later, they went on to get married with Reverend Wilson presiding.

Chapter 34
River: The Finished Story

The story about River and Hank always enlightened Terry. His father commented that when he read this passage he felt like Hank, the runaway slave. Terry's father remembered when the police officers were chasing him the night Uncle Jesse was murdered. Terry remembered a vague connection with his father as he wrote this passage. Terry also remembered that this scream was abruptly interrupted with the phone call from his mother, notifying him of his father's predicament.

After months and years of screaming to understand his purpose in life, Terry began to study all of his writings. He became baffled with the River passage, something just piqued his curiosity about this passage. One day he decided to concentrate on screaming about River. He sat in his most comfortable chair with his journal and pen in hand and his shoes off his feet. Unlike the screams with Louis Armstrong after that salesmen rang the doorbell and interrupted, the story of Hank and River came back to him on his first attempt to finish the passage and answer his curiosity. Hank was able to escape from the Dawson's plantation and run for days to get to freedom. When River and Hank finally got to freedom, the phone rang and ended Terry's screaming. Terry wrote and finished the story about River after hours of screaming.

A couple of days after the escape, Hank and River came upon a rather large plantation. Hank was carrying River with his hand over his mouth, casing the plantation from a distance. There were over two hundred slaves in the fields and many milling around the barns.

It was early in the morning. Hank was hungry, and he knew that River was also starving. Stealing any type of food was on Hank's mind. The blanket was kept, but the bread and potatoes were lost during the chase.

Hank stood in the shadow of the trees and watched a white man screaming with fury at a young black slave boy near the big house. He was teaching the boy how to cut wood. Hank observed this spectacle for an hour. The man was small in stature and was getting tired of teaching. As the man took out his whip, River, being restless, jumped out of Hank's arms and ran toward the man. Hank started to run after River. The man heard something moving quickly through the tall grass. River reached the man, barking and wagging his tail. The puppy, which hadn't eaten in days, was on the thin side. When River reached the man, Hank stopped about twenty yards away from the field. The man looked up. The white man saw Hank and reached for his gun. Letting the man know his purpose, Hank called out, "River, come 'ere, boy!" The man acknowledged the puppy's ownership and hesitantly motioned for Hank to come over.

The man introduced himself proudly saying, "I am Philip Garner. And, what is your name?" Hank didn't open his mouth. He was terrified that disclosing any name would reveal his runaway status. It was only seven days after leaving Dawson's Plantation. Garner heard a big growl while rubbing the puppy—a big growl from either Hank's stomach or River's stomach. Astonished by the tones of hunger, Garner quickly asked, "Boy, are you hungry?" Hank immediately nodded yes. Mr. Garner asked Hank to finish teaching the boy how to cut the wood. Hank started teaching the boy and was cutting most of the wood for the boy as Garner watched. River jumped out of Garner's arm and ran to lie near the big house.

Garner asked, "How long you had River?"

Hank said, "I got him when he was a week or so."

Garner asked, "How did he get the name River?"

"Well Mr. Garner, I was walking along the great river and looked over in a patch of grass and there he was. A little long-bodied, short-dog pup. He looked like he was lost and hungry like me. So I named him River! I don't know what kind of dog he is, just a black dog."

Confident, Hank aimed to impress Garner. He saw a sign and read it. "No trespassing, huh. I guess River and I needs to be going, sir."

"What did you say?" Garner asked.

Hank said it again, "No trespassing. So we'd best be on our way. I don't aim to anger your boss, sir, so I'd best be going."

Garner didn't say a word. The little boy said, "He can read!"

Garner turned and walked towards the back door of the house. He picked up River, turned to Hank and said, "You can read? I've never seen a nigger read!"

Mr. Garner went into the house and talked with his wife. He showed her the puppy and talked about the reading Nigger.

Mr. Garner felt a sudden fondness for the smart black man and his charismatic dog. He was intrigued. He then said, "I want him to eat with us. I want to welcome him!" His wife looked stunned, almost faint. Her last words, were "The Nigger?" Her husband shocked her, and she fell to her chaise, short of breath.

Meanwhile, the slave boy gave Hank the history about Mr. Garner. "Mister, you lucky you ain't full of buckshot; Garner hates us folk. He whipped and killed over ten since I turned eight last summer. Them men and women is dead for no reason. Mama think he gonna kill me, too. You'd better run before he come back with the overseers."

Hank gave no answer. The boy knew Garner better than he did. Hank trembled as the boy's warning echoed in his head. Hank started stepping back from the woodpile. Before he could take a second step, Garner came through the porch door saying, "Y'all finish yet?"

Ben said, "No, sir!"

Hank stopped his motion and trembled with fear. He only thought of two things as Garner got closer to him: he'd run or he'd say his favorite bible verse. As others started looking around from the household, from the sides of barns, and outhouses, Hank burst out into verse with "The Lawd is my shepherd, I shall not want. He leadeth me…"

Garner finished the twenty-third Psalm with Hank. They laughed.

Garner all of a sudden said, "Sir, I don't know your name, but I want you to join me for today's meal."

Hank said, "Surely, Mr. Garner, I'm mighty hungry! Call me Joecum, Mr. Garner."

"Mr. Joecum, please come on in and talk with Ma-Tina."

Ma-Tina was the house cook in charge of everything, even though Mrs. Garner would claim credit. Ma-Tina had orders to fix a tub of hot water, get shoes, socks, a pair of pants, a shirt, sweater, coat, hat, and a blanket and to fix a great meal.

Word had gotten to the slaves about a reading free man in the big house being treated like the mayor. Within an hour, all slaves had gathered around the house to see Joecum. The butler, Tiny, fixed the steamy tub of soap water. When Hank entered the room, Mr. Garner said, "Tiny, did you set everything up?"

Tiny properly replied, "Yes sir, Master Garner!"

Garner replied, "Please take care of Mr. Joecum."

Hank had already repeated the twenty-third Psalm five times as he walked to the bathroom. Tiny whispered to Hank when Garner left the room, "What type of nigger is you to get royalty treatment? Who are you?" Hank said nothing. "Did you put the root on ol' Garner?" Tiny asked.

Hank said "No!" immediately. He did not want to be associated with the demons.

Hank said, "I don't know why I'm getting this treatment, but I will say that I feel like the hog getting dressed up before Sunday dinner."

Tiny then said, "You got him with your reading. I say you leave after dinner; that man may snap out of this with a whipping at the end of the night.

Hank quickly said, "I'll go after dinner."

Tiny then asked, "You know any table manners?"

Hank replied "No!"

When you eat, work from the outside to the inside with the forks and knives.

Hank had a look of confusion on his face. Tiny went to the kitchen to get forks and spoons then gave a five minute lesson in table manners while Hank lounged in the bathtub. While Tiny was returning the silverware, Hank said, "Thank ya, Lawd!" before allowing his eyes to close.

Within ninety minutes, Ma-Tina was done. Ben, the slave-boy, had finished washing and feeding River.

To Mrs. Garner's bewilderment, Hank ate a full course meal at the big table with the servant. When Mrs. Garner saw the black man dressed with good clothing, shaven and hair neatly trimmed she fell in love with his power, demeanor and curious disposition. She turned red in the face.

"Mr. Joecum looks smart," Ma-Tina whispered to Tiny.

The slave women, peeking in the window, fell instantly in love, and the slave men smiled with great hope and pride.

Mrs. Garner became more vocal at the dinner.

Mr. Garner asked no questions, but he told story after story, probably lie after lie. Hank talked about the bible and stories he had heard people tell at Dawson's Plantation. Hank told him how he learned how to read by befriending an old black freed man. Garner kept saying, "Amazing!"

Then Garner explained "It's simply amazing that I can sit you down here and treat you like a friend. You are black and can read just like me and you know and recite my favorite bible verse. It's amazing." Hank just nodded his head.

Tiny was giving hints to Hank before he made a bad move. Hank, hungry after over one-hundred-and-fifty miles of foot travel and three days without solid food was too nervous to eat anything with civility. He took the cornbread in hand and gobbled a decent bit down. Tiny winked okay.

Afterwards Hank used a fork and spoon for the first time; it was shaky in the beginning. The rice fell off and the beans didn't pick up but everything was getting to his mouth. Tiny was kind enough to place the napkin in his lap.

Ma-Tina prepared the best dinner of the year for the newcomer. Hank ate two servings of everything. He was full to the brim. Mr. Garner said, "There'll be enough for tomorrow." Hank thought to himself as being the fattened pig for Sunday dinner. He said, "Sir, I can't stay here tonight. I must be headed north before nightfall."

It was approaching late evening time. Hank had been treated better in the past five hours of the day than his entire lifetime.

He told Mr. Garner that he was thankful. Mr. Garner said, while patting River on the head, "Don't worry, Joecum."

Mr. Garner then asked Hank, "Why don't you let me and my family keep the young pup while you journey home? He reminds me of our dog we lost a couple of weeks ago. She was too friendly to the slaves, so we started tying her up. She ran away and we haven't heard from her since."

"Sir, I'se can tell you really wants River, but I feel the way you felt about that dog that went away. I'se got to keep River." Hank started taking off his new clothing.

Mr. Garner said. "Keep it, it yours! You've been a delightful visitor. It's silly of me to think that you would part with such a fine dog. I understand."

So with the white man's warm clothing and a clean blanket, a clean body, shoes, and a cap, Hank fell to his knees to catch River and praise God for the miracle.

Hank said goodbye and recited the twenty-third Psalm for the final time. Mr. Garner smiled and said it simultaneously. Hank returned to the woods near the firewood pile and headed North with River. Hank vowed to always remember Ma-Tina, Mr. Garner, and Ben. He also decided to keep the name of his father. "Hank Joecum, that's what I'll call myself, River. Hank Joecum." Hank was prouder than he had ever been. They slept, with full bellies, under an oak tree that night.

The slaves knew something happened to Mr. Garner. They blamed or explained the entire occurrence on the fact that Joecum could read and he recited the bible to Mr. Garner. Every slave thereafter wanted to get the Joecum treatment and search for the bible and preachers to teach them how to read and recite.

Before the evening was over, Mrs. Garner gathered all the field hands and house slaves. She vowed to kill all who took this event past this plantation

215

or spoke of Mr. Joecum again in her presence or any other white person's. She told her children to never mention this night to anyone. NEVER!

The proud twosome came across many adventures while journeying north. It took three months to touch Maryland, and things changed for the duo. Hank managed to secure a part-time job cleaning for a printing press owned by C.M. Clay. Hank didn't write articles but understood that Mr. Clay was fair to give him work. Hank was happy beyond words.

As Hank fixed Mr. Clay's storage area for bedding that night, he called River to his side. River sprung into his lap and licked Hank like he never had. Hank's heart was filled with total joy and freedom for the first time in his life.

Early that morning, Hank awoke to the sound of coughing, choking, and hacking. River had moved to the corner of the room and balled up like a fur ball. Hank scampered over to comfort River with water from his water dish. As River's last breath came, Hank saw an apparition hovering over them. Hank cried, "Why?" The angel said, "The Lord is my shepherd, I shall not want." Hank quickly joined in with the angel, and as they neared the final verse, the angel vanished. Hank cried through the night and buried River in Clay's backyard just before sunrise. That same morning, after millions of steps, Jim, a runaway slave from Smith's Plantation, looked down and saw the faint eyes of a puppy. The howling from the overseer's bloodhound shook Jim's concentration. Jim ignored the puppy. The puppy moaned and gave a desperate cry for affection. If Jim had shown the puppy any attention, his steps would have made him trip over the puppy's dead mother. Tragically he stayed on pace and stepped over the dead body.

When they finally caught Jim, he could only think of himself. He didn't even recognize the beauty of the overseer's horse. Jim never recognized life's smallest things. Sad to say, he never got to the river because he never got on the right path of life. His body hung from an oak tree, as the puppy balled up beside the tree's base, River moaned and desperately cried for Jim's soul.

Terry came out of this screaming expedition with sweat and tears on his face. He had realized the underlying messages in this passage. One was that he should care about all living things and enjoy life in any situation. Secondly, he realized that you never know when you come across an angel, so you should treat everyone as if they were an angel. Thirdly, that he understood mean men would treat you equally if they knew you had an angelic force with you. He realized that not all men, like in the case of Jim, the other runaway slave, will ever understand the glory of God's kingdom. And those that do attempt to help these men, will be greatly saddened by their demise. Terry also saw the importance of education. Finally, Terry saw the possibility of losing an angel in his life. He could not picture what angel would leave him. Terry quickly got on his knees and prayed asking God to protect and keep his family from death's hands.

Chapter 35
The Gift is Delivered

Veronica was going into her last month of pregnancy. Terry and Veronica had enjoyed two years of blissful marriage and now God had presented the gift of life to them. Terry had never been so proud of his wife and his life. He couldn't wait to take care of his family.

On March 18, Terry Veron Foster, a healthy baby boy was born. Exactly nine months after Terry finished the River passage and prayed to the Lord, Veron was delivered. But Veronica, the angel in his life, died during the difficult labor. Terry's emotions were unstable for many months. Terry had lost the only woman that mattered to him. He had lost his best friend. Terry knew that she went on to do better things, and The Holy Spirit comforted Terry with his new gift of life. Terry would be the best father for their child. Everyday Terry saw Veronica in the eyes of Veron. He found his purpose in life.

Since he started screaming, his life had been better because he had gotten to know himself. The screaming allowed Terry Foster to prosper through hard times, enjoy good times and help friends. He even looked forward to seeing how he could defeat Satan's attempt to bring his friends and strangers to hell.

Terry was challenged again—this time with being a single father.

Terry had to become a real man—a real man who overcame insecurities about commitment to a woman; a real man who taught others about faith in the Lord and lending a helping hand. He discovered that a real man was one who is strong in the knowledge of where he came from—one who can conquer anything with God, patience, and discipline. One who knows that patience knows all answers.

There were no words to show how much he missed Veronica, and he didn't know the reason why she passed. Terry knew that his reason for living was to make sure his son would live in the light of the Lord. His life's lessons are what he would use to build and mold Veron's character.

Twelve years later, Veron surprised Terry and the entire church. Veron, a mature, twelve-year old, sang his first solo in the choir. Veron led the choir in its rendition of *Order My Steps.* Terry had yet another reason to be proud of his son. After Veron finished singing, he stood up and spoke in tongues. Terry sat motionless and listened to every word that was said. Reverend Wilson had the same astonished look he had when Terry spoke in tongues some twenty years ago. The entire church looked at Veron. Some of the missionaries threw their arms up in praise. Reverend Wilson looked to the audience and said, "Our young folks may know the Lord better than any man. Let us pray."

As Veron sat in the choir with his eyes on his father, Terry winked and nodded his head. Veron did not know what had happened. The reverend counseled the father and son in his office after the services. Veron was visibly shaken and embarrassed. While Veron sat in his chair with his head down, Terry said, "You're okay, Veron. You did a great job singing."

Veron said, "Thank you, I was not even scared until I started shaking from the excitement."

Terry said, "Don't worry. It's happened to me and your great-great-grandmother and now it has happened to you. It is nothing to be afraid of, be proud and thankful you have this gift."

Veron said, "Yes, sir. What gift?"

Reverend Wilson then interrupted and said, "Veron, you did a great job singing. I want you to read chapters thirteen and fourteen of Corinthians to understand what happened today. Okay?"

Veron smiled and appeared to regain his confidence because the two men he respected more than anyone on earth had just given him a compliment and justification for what went on in the sanctuary. Terry sent Veron out to the car to wait. When Veron left the office, Reverend Wilson said, "Just like his father."

They laughed.

Terry said, "He's a good boy."

Terry then asked, "Rev, you know I need the videotape of the church service." Réverend Wilson smiled, went to the VCR, and pressed the eject button. He handed the tape to Terry with a little remorse.

Terry then said, "Rev, I understood what Veron said."

Reverend Wilson looked at Terry in amazement. The reverend didn't say a word.

Terry then said, "Rev, it was a rehearsal of sorts and my son, Veron just stood up in front of this congregation and said his part." A great silence came between the reverend and Terry.

Terry then finished. "Veron said, 'Lord, this is your gift from my father's family. These are the needles we have found who have lived by the Word. We hope that the camels shall pass through the eyes of these needles. Lord, this is our gift to you.'"

Terry had tears in his eyes, and said "Do you remember when you met my grandmother?"

The reverend nodded yes.

Terry asked, "Do you remember the quilt with the haystack and needles she showed you?"

The reverend nodded yes again.

As Terry wiped a tear from his eye, he said, "Rev, Veron will present Grandma's quilt on Judgement Day."

"Is that so, Terry?" Reverend Wilson asked.

Terry nodded yes.

Staring into Terry's eyes, Reverend Wilson said with a mixture of great honor, joy, and a hint of sadness, "Judgement Day is very near, teach him all that you know. Tell your friends and families to get their lives together because the Lord will come soon."

Terry smiled and said, "I will do that which is my purpose in life. I will teach my son everything about being a real man. I will let my people know that the Lamb comes soon. I will live my life by His words."

"That's all that was ever asked of us, Terry, that's all Jesus ever asked."

They both then said, "Amen."

THE END